T r o p i c a l

REEF FISHES

An Awareness Guide on fishes from the Indo-Pacific Realm

Great Barrier Reef, Australia
Indonesia Archipelago
Bunaken Marine Park, North Sulawesi
Maldives
Malaysia
Philippines
Thailand
South Pacific Islands

OCEAN
GEOGRAPHIC
POCKET BOOK SERIES

Michael AW
Laura Woodward

Photographer: Michael AW
Authors: Michael AW & Laura Woodward
Scientific Editor: Dr. Gerald Allen
Consulting Editors: Dr. Maria Kavallaris & Sophia Symeou
Art Direction & Concept: Michael AW
Producer Assistant: Sandra Hejtmanek
E6 Processing: Colour Development (Sydney)
Printed by: Print Resources Sdn. Bhd. (Malaysia)

Publisher
OCEAN GEOGRAPHIC Media
62 Bellamy Street
Pennant Hills, NSW 2120
Australia
Produced by Ocean Discoverers
All Photographs are Copyright © 1994 Michael AW
Manuscripts are Copyright © 1994 Michael AW & Laura Woodward

National Library of Australia Cataloguing-in-Publication Entry
AW Michael/ Laura Woodward
Tropical Reef Fishes -A Marine Awareness Guide
ISBN 0 646 20473 4

CONTENTS

The Indo-Pacific Realm stretches from the East African coast to Easter Island in the South Pacific, and north to the Hawaiian Islands. As most offspring of coral reef animals spend some of their early life as planktonic larvae, they travel freely on the highway of continental and regional currents across this region.

The heartland of this region is the Indo-Pacific Archipelago comprised of Indonesia, the Philippines, New Guinea and Northern Australia; a vast area with thousands of reefs and islands. Here lies the richest biological diversity of marine fauna in the world.

Indonesia, ideally situated geographically and biologically representing the heart of the core, has the greatest concentration of fauna. To the east, as the distance increases across the Pacific, diversity of fauna progressively declines in richness. To the west, diversity decreases by about a third and remains constant around the Indian ocean reefs. It is estimated that over 3000 species of fish are found in the Indonesian archipelago compared with 2500 in the Philippines, 1300 in the Australian Great Barrier Reef and 800 in the Red sea.

Ichthyologists frequently use Damselfishes (*Pomacentridae)*, a prominent inhabitant of the reef, to illustrate the richness of an area. Indonesia has 132 different species of Damselfishes, New Guinea has 103, and the Great Barrier Reef 97. Again the greater the distance from the core, the fewer the species count; the Solomons have only 98, Vanuatu 78, Fiji 58, Tahiti 30 and Easter Island 3, of which two are endemic.

Using the analogy of shopping in a downtown supermarket and a suburban corner store, our 'shopping list' for fish pictures centered around the Indonesian-Australian archipelago with 'Bunaken Manado-Tua Marine Park' of North Sulawesi, Indonesia, being the complex we visited most frequently.

"Save the Environment" has become a trendy phrase. Conserving energy, recycling paper, glass, plastics and water, saving the rainforest and improving the quality of air are some of the more popular surface measures that have been taken.

In the marine world there are many campaigns about saving the whales and dolphins. They are cute and adorable. Through the media, movies and moving stories, we have learned to love and make a stand to protect these beautiful creatures. But what about the smaller animals of the ocean? What about the coral reef? Apart from identifying a few butterflyfishes or two what else do most of us really know? How can we attempt to save an environment that we know so little about or have so little affinity with?

Some of us are not aware that there is only one ocean in the world, a vast mass of water that covers two thirds of this planet and in its depths contains life that was around on this planet long before human or dinosaurs ever were.

Understanding, Appreciation and Love Begets Preservation and Protection.

In the first of this series of marine awareness guides, you will discover the world of tropical reef fishes; where each family lives, their lifestyle, and how they reproduce. They might have small brains but they have developed some very advanced and bizarre survival techniques as well as having the ability to think, to know what is good and what is bad and who are their enemies and friends. Some live in harems, others in schools while some of them lead a monogamous or bohemian lifestyle. In fish societies there are also ranks and file, parental responsibilities, sex reversal and communal living arrangements among families and friends. *A Marine Awareness Guide to Tropical Reef Fishes* is only a brief insight into their world, but we hope that it will enhance your awareness and help you develop or continue your love affair with the sea.

Remove any plastic or garbage you see on the reef. Adopt the T.O.G. (Take Only Garbage) attitude.

Even if it is legal, set an exemplary example by not removing anything such as shells, corals or fish either dead or alive from the sea.

Do not throw anything into the sea, even if it is bio-degradable.

If you are a snorkeller or scuba diver, remember it is man made technology that allows you to venture into the aquatic realm, we are only intruders. Respect the inhabitants of the ocean and minimize damage to the reef with your fins.

Marine photographers, it is not worth killing for a picture. Use your breathing techniques to maintain buoyancy to minimize damage to corals and other invertebrates. Do not harass your subject. Use your pictures to promote the beauty of the sea.

Support only environmentally conscious resort and travel operators.

Report to the Department of Tourism, or Ministry of Environment within that jurisdiction, any observations of damage or practises that could be damaging to the marine environment.

Learn more about marine animals by attending marine ecology programs.

Participate in Eco-Tourism expeditions.

Contribute to the preservation of the ocean with positive suggestions.

Share knowledge with others in a positive manner.

Write and complain to magazines, newspapers or book publishers who publish pictures that show harassments to animals or articles that are ecologically offensive.

Above all take environmental issues seriously and believe that however little your contribution, **You can make a difference.**

Ocean Discoverers.

Tropical reefs are one of the most beautiful places on Earth. Nowhere else on this planet can such diversity of animals living and growing together in such magnitude be found.

Each time we venture into this environment, we will learn and witness a little more about the magical creation of Nature's Richest Realm. An almost silent world where the dependency and sustenance of each member in the web of life is closely intertwined, more so than any place on earth.

Tropical Reef fishes are the pulse and soul of coral reefs, contributing to her health and ecological well being. Whilst the plants of a reef use sunlight and carbon dioxide to produce energy rich organisms, herbivorous feeders like the Surgeon fish remove algae from the reef to allow young corals to develop.

Fishes such as Butterflyfishes, Parrotfishes and Wrasses play their role on the reefs food chain by feeding on coral polyps and inevitably producing reef sediment, which provides a home to many marine invertebrates that live on the reef bed. In turn these small animals are the food source for such fishes as Gobies, Blennies, Scorpionfishes, and Sandperches who all feed solely on benthic (bottom living) animals like crabs and shrimp.

Most fishes eggs', or larvae, float on the surface of the ocean before settling down to live on the reef. The top layer of the sea is literally a 'seafood soup' created by the 'Mothers of the Reef'. This soup is the food source of many aquatic animals including pelagic fishes, which are of course an important food source for human being. Nature works in mysterious and magnificent ways.

The importance of preserving the coral reef environment cannot be emphasized enough. Its survival is dependent on all its inhabitants and on us, and ultimately our survival is directly or indirectly linked to the sea.

Tips to Catch

Patience

Underwater photography first evolved as a craft, then later as a true art form to celebrate the beauty of the sea. For those of you who are not acquainted with my fish pictures, they are made with simple compositions, one light source, one standard film, and they convey a single message.

First lets consider fish photography as the application of a craft. Just like an artist or sculptor or dentist they all have one thing in common - the right tool for the right job.

All my images are made with Nikon 801s systems in an underwater housing. Small fishes are taken with a Nikon 105mm f2.8 macro lens and many of the larger species with my favorite 60mm macro f2.8 lens.

I prefer to use the Ikelite housing over the aluminium version mainly due to its light weight, user friendly controls and the great after sales service. I take at least two Ikelite housings mounted with 105mm and 60mm ports, to avoid the necessity of changing port and with the luxury of Laura assisting I can carry both of them in a single dive.

Another very important tool is the flash unit, especially when working with macro lenses on 1:1 capability. The depth of field is critical, and powerful underwater strobes are required to overcome this. For this purpose I use the Ikelite 150D strobes which are equipped with the convenience of self contained rechargeable battery packs.

To effectively light up my fish, I have to reposition my light source frequently. I use a rigid and yet flexible jointed strobe arm system made by Associated Design & Manufacturing Company in Virginia. Fuji Velvia is my film of choice, chosen for its strong colours and grainless characteristics. Its high contrast and intense saturation of reds and greens is marvellous for

iSHES ON FilM

f the Essence

close up wide-angle, and macro work. All my films are processed in normal development time at 'Color Development, Sydney. I do not use any color filters whilst taking the pictures or enhancement processes during color separation.

To make a good fish picture, remember this: Patience is of the essense and you have to love your subject. Fishes are not used to seeing a noisy four legged animal with strange contraption that blows bubbles, so it is necessary to begin with a bonding period before getting down to the important business. Unless you have lots of energy and like pictures of fish tails, chasing fish is the worst thing you can do. With the contents of this book, learn about fishes habitat, their behavior, their lifestyle and you will soon be able to take some great pictures in their environment doing fishy things! Great pictures take time.

Having said that, time underwater is limited by our intake of nitrogen. Once past the time limit we are subject to the curse of the crippling bends and may never take another fish picture again. To monitor time underwater or to calculate required decompression time I use a hoseless air-integrated dive computer. Yes, fish photography is a risky business.

In each family I have included some additional hints from my experience with some of the species. Remember, every fish is a thinking fish, they tend to vary in their behaviour.

Enjoy your time spent with them.

Additionally, alongside each picture, I have also shared with you information on the lens used and the residence of the subject. You might wish to join us in the near future in our underwater sojourns at Ocean Discoverers

We look forward to diving in the same Ocean with you.

How to use this book

This book is a marine awareness guide to the most commonly found Tropical Reef fish families in the Indo-Pacific ocean, from the shores of East Africa and the Red Sea to the Hawaiian Islands and French Polynesia.
Covering 33 families of tropical reef fishes, the criteria for selection of each family is based on its abundance and popularity on the reef, that is the most common fishes that you are likely to encounter whether as a snorkeller, diver, or just fish watching.

General information and species of fish that are featured are examples only. This is not intended as a fish identification book.
At the top of each left hand page, the family common and scientific name shall be given. The scientific classification used for identifying fish can be confusing for the non-scientist. The commonly used terms in this book are species, genus (or genera) and family. The species of an animal is at the base of the classification tree. A genus is composed of a group of separate species with many similar external and internal features. The family is then composed of all genera that have overall similar characteristics and share a common line of ancestry.

For ease of use we have divided the families, into 3 colour coded sections;

Blue Water Cruisers
Pelagic free swimming fishes found in the open ocean or on the outer edge of coral reefs.

The Bottom Dweller
Fishes usually found living on the reef flat, reef wall, or sea bed.

Hole and Crevice Residents
Fishes that are usually found in holes and crevices of the coral reef.

Additional reference aids to help you include a coloured vertical box at the side of each right hand page. The coloured frame instantly identifies which section of the book the family belongs and its habitat.

Example
Family name: Chaetontidae
Ornate Butterflyfish
Genus / Genera: *Chaetodon*
Closely related butterflyfishes
Species: *ornatissimus*
name of species
i.e.Ornate Butterflyfish

All fish possess a few distinguishing characteristics that separate it from others. Like a detective, when identifying the family that a fish belongs to you are looking for a combination of clues. These include, bodyshape, size, number and type of fins, any distinguishing features, and habitat.

For ease of description on the size of a fish, we generally use the following classifications:

WHAT Fish is THAT ?

Tiny - as long as your little finger or less
Small - as long as your hand or less
Medium - as long as your forearm or less
Large - as long as your arm or bigger

Was the fish sticklike? Did it have a disc-like body, one that looks round or oval in a side or top profile, or a more solid heavybody? Was the tail rounded or forked? Were there one or two dorsal fins? Did it have a long snout or beaky mouth like the parrotfish? Did it have spikes or long whiskers (barbels)? Where did you see them? Were they sitting on coral? These are all questions that will help point you in the right direction.

EXTERNAL FEATURES of BONY FISHES

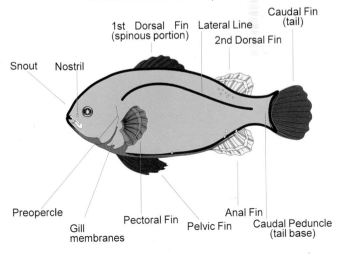

Caudal Fin (tail)
1st Dorsal Fin (spinous portion)
Lateral Line
2nd Dorsal Fin
Snout
Nostril
Preopercle
Gill membranes
Pectoral Fin
Pelvic Fin
Anal Fin
Caudal Peduncle (tail base)

We Live within One   Round body of Blue   wa
One Body of Water sustain   all Life

(Beneath

The Blue Water Cruisers

Pelagic or
free swimming fishes
found in the open
OCEAN
or on
Coral reefs

Pipefishes & Trumpetfish
(Syngnathidae & Aulstornidae)

We have presented Trumpetfish and Pipefishes together in this section as they are both characterized by a long slender stick-like body and elongated snouts. However while Trumpetfish are free swimmers on the reef, Pipefishes are bottom dwellers found on the substratum.

Pipefishes (Syngnathidae)

Pipefishes have an elongated snout and a face reminiscent of a seahorse, which is not surprising since they belong to the same family (Sygnathidae). Further detailed inspection reveals a single dorsal fin, no pelvic fin, and a very small anal fin. Often their trunks are striped or in some cases a series of bands encircle the body all the way to their caudal fin or tail.

Pipefishes are always there but rarely seen. Timid diurnal creatures and feeble swimmers they simply lay on the reef floor well camouflaged, float about either in caves or out in the open, or hide in crevices or around wrecks. They use their elongated mouths like a pipette when feeding on small crustaceans, sucking in water which contains their prey with a quick forceful suction. This family of 200 species of 55 genera live in shallow waters in diverse habitats.

Trumpetfish (Aulostomidae)

A single species family, Trumpetfish (Aulostomus chinensis) reach up to 80cm(36") in length. Active predators of fishes found in tropical and sub-tropical shallows around the world, they live on the reef amongst coral trees and crinoids. Trumpetfish is a common sighting in the Indo-Pacific and looks like a drifting stick. Their body is solid and stick-like, and it has a trumpet-like face with a barbel on the chin. The pelvic fins are located at the rear of the body and the row of sharp spines on the back are only raised in defence.

A slow swimmer, the Trumpetfish relies on camouflage and stealth to hunt by ambush, sneaking up on a victim by concealing itself behind the bodies of larger fish or hiding patiently in coral outcrops. Camouflage artists, they are well known for their abilities to change colour almost instantly to blend in with the background.

Making little Pipers and Trumpeters

Pipefishes have a unique method of breeding. An elaborate courtship of entwining bodies, is often initiated by the female. She eventually passes her eggs to the male who incubates them either in his pouch or by attaching them beneath his tail. The pregnant male then carries them until they hatch. The hatchlings are usually miniatures of their parents. As far as we know Trumpetfish do not incubate eggs, but shed them in open water like most other fishes.

Taking Pictures of these Slender Folks

The problem is framing them. Having a longish body, a frontal shot will end up with no nose room but plenty of head room. Try positioning them diagonally or go for a close-up head shot.

BRONZE TRUMPET FISH
Aulostomus sp.
60mm f2.8 / Bunaken, Nth Sulawesi

BANDED PIPEFISH
Corythoichthys intestinalis
60mm f2.8 / Bali, Indonesia

Rock Cods & Basslets
(Serranidae)

Rockcods, Coral Trout, Groupers, Sea Basses, Basslets, Soapfishes and Podges are all common names given to members of this huge family. Due to the diversity within the family, in recent years some genera have been classified as subfamilies of the Serranidae family tree.

Rockcods or Groupers
Subfamily : Epinephelinae

What's My Name?

Groupers, Rockcods and Coral trouts are classified in the subfamily Epinephelinae. Despite their many different names the family can be identified by their solid torpedo shaped body with prominent jaws, canine teeth, continuous dorsal fin with an obvious spiny section, mottled patterns and disruptive camouflage colours.

Groupers are large fish and make up more than 150 species in over 20 genera. Some grow to at least 2 metres(6ft), weigh up to 200kg(440lb), and can live for more than 50 years. Other rockcod members are small to medium sized fish. They are reef dwellers living a solitary existence, frequently with only one or two cod living on any part of the reef.

Strictly Carnivorous

All members of these families are carnivores equipped with several rows of sharp teeth. Additionally fish-eating species are usually distinguished by their prominent canines at the front of the jaw.

Feeding mainly on fish and crustaceans they are the top reef predators, usually lurking in the reef waiting to ambush their prey. Dining at dusk they use their large elastic mouths to create a suction to pull the prey in and then seize it with their teeth.

Four Saddle Rockcod
Ephinephelus spilotoceps
60mm f2.8 / Bunaken, Nth. Sulawesi

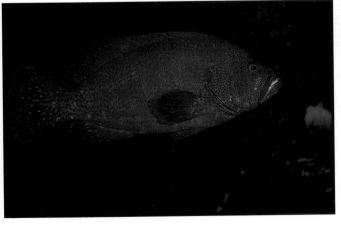

Tomato Rockcod
Cephalopholis sonnerati
60mm f2.8 / New Britain, New Guinea

Rock Cods & Basslets
(Serranidae)

Who has a Better Sex Life?

Most groupers in the sub-family *Epinephelinae,* start life as females and, after one or two years of spawning, change into males. When it is time to procreate they gather in pairs, or in a group, in the twilight at the outer edge of the reef.

Spawning begins when the female, laden with eggs, approaches a prospective mate. She begins by swimming in an S-curve formation, with her fins fully erect, and then quivers in front of her male. If the mate is keen he will follow her in a slow jerky exaggerated swimming pattern. The male nudges the female's distended belly at which point she blanches and the male develops a conspicuous barred pattern. The S-curving and jerk-swimming accelerate to a crescendo when the pair dash up from the bottom to shed their eggs and sperm.

Gifted with a bizarre variation of hermaphroditism, the *Serraninae* subfamily, found mainly in the Atlantic and East Pacific, have what we would perhaps call a great sex life; certainly an interesting one. The scientific term is "Simultaneous Hermaphroditism" meaning that each individual produces both eggs and sperm. Quite simply this means that when it comes to spawning both the female and male alternate their roles, one lays eggs while the other sheds sperm and then vice versa.

For this sub-family, after the first spawning the pair resumes the courtship with the partners reversing roles. The couple engaged in spawning will continue for several hours alternating the male and female roles.

Portrait of Rock Cod

There are the bold and there are the timid. Fishes of these families are both. They are territorial hence it is best to photograph them in their territory. You will find them looking at you beneath table coral or wreck sites. A period of bonding is required to take successful pictures.

Red Barred Rockcod
Ephinephelus fasciatus
60mm f2.8 / Bunaken, Nth. Sulawesi

Coral Rockcod
Cephalopholis miniata
60mm f2.8 /
Great Barrier Reef, Australia

Rock Cods & Basslets
(Serranidae)

Basslets
Sub-family:Anthiinae

These pretty fish, sometimes referred to as the "fairies" of the reef, are typically seen in large congregations. They provide a plethora of colour to the reef, seen in groups flushed with shades of electric pink, yellow, violet, green, orange and magenta. Conspicuous by their abundance they form an important part of coral reef fauna.

Recognizing Basslets

If you see a group of brightly coloured small slender fish hovering above hard coral, an educated guess would be that they are basslets. Other 'tell-tale' clues to look for are their forked caudal tail closely resembling a 'mermaids' tail. All of them sport a long continuous dorsal fin and long anal and pelvic fins which are filamentous and flimsy in texture.

Reaching a maximum length of 15cm(7"), the males are usually more colourful than females and some of them have delicate extended third spines protruding from their dorsal fin or tail.

Family Affairs

Basslets belong to a family of 23 genera with nearly 100 species and are distributed in all tropical oceans, although they are especially abundant on the reefs of the Indo-Pacific. They are gregarious fish and can often be seen feeding on zooplankton, or foraging in large groups among coral outcrops or on the reef's edge during the day. At the first approach of danger however they quickly descend to shelter among corals or rocks, which also offers them protection whilst sleeping at night.

Many species live in specific habitats of corals or caves but can typically be found at drop-offs at the reef's edge at depths of up to 45m(150ft).
Basslets are tasty prey for Moray Eels (*Muraenidae*) and Scorpionfish (*Scorpaenidae*) as well as for their bigger cousins, Rockcod or Groupers.

Pink Bassler(male) with false cleaner wrasse
Pseudanthias hypselosoma
105mm f2.8 / GREAT BARRIER REEF, AUSTRALIA

Pinkish Bassler(female)
Pseudanthais hypselosoma
105mm f2.8 / BUNAKEN, Nth. SULAWESI

Rock Cods & Basslets
(Serranidae)

Season of Sex Changes

Basslets are hermaphrodites. They start life as females and change to males in later life. The stimulus for the sex change has been attributed to size, age or the removal of the dominant male in a group.

This removal results in the biggest female changing her colour pattern and sex to that of the dominant male predecessor and taking control over his group of subordinate females. The complete physical switch is complete within a couple of days.

Upon the dawning of the spawning season, small groups of females and males split off from the reef and regroup near their pre-selected mating sites on the outer reef. While some males may be territorial, others may not be. All males however erect their fins and quickly change into courtship colours.

The time for their communion occurs after dusk which is preceded by the male display of zigzag swimming and dipping up and down. Spawning for the female basslet is a very brief affair involving no foreplay from her partner. If a female responds to the male 'strut' she approaches the male and they briefly come together for a few seconds when the eggs and sperm are instantly shed. Not having much time for such 'nonsense' the female spawns only once a night and then returns to her activities, while the male continues to spawn with as many females as possible.

Spawning by several pairs may take place simultaneously. Their pelagic eggs hatch in under 24 hours.

Photographing the Razzle-Dazzle

I have always enjoyed taking pictures of basslets. They are extremely colourful and a joy to watch. These dainty fishes almost seem to communicate with you. Quite often you will see one looking straight at you for a few seconds before dashing off in another direction. A 105mm lens is essential.

SCALEFIN BASSLET (MALE)
Pseudanthias squamipinnis
105mm f2.8 / Bunaken, Nth. Sulawesi

ORANGE STRIPED BASSLET
Pseudanthias fasciatus
105mm f2.8 / Ambon, Indonesia

Sweetlips
(Haemulidae)

Perhaps it is the gentle and sweet appearance of the *Haemulidae* that earn it the common name of Sweetlips instead of its other more appropriate name of Gruntfish. Sweetlips of the Atlantic and East Pacific oceans, such as the genera *Haemulon and Pomadasys*, emit rude grunting noises made by the grinding of their pharyngeal teeth and when this sound is further amplified by their bladder, they are one of the noisiest inhabitants of the tropical coral reef.

Sweet Features

Sweetlips resemble the laterally compressed body shape of Snappers (*Lutjanidae*) but they look much friendlier with a smaller mouth, smacking thick lips and no canine teeth.

Predominantly the adult species are bright yellow with black stripes or spots. The juveniles vary dramatically from the adult, being either black and white in colour, or sporting white spots with dark brown segments. One prime example is the juvenile of *Plectorhinchus chaetodontoides,* commonly known as the Clown Sweetlips, due to its resemblance to Anemonefishes (*Amphiprion*) in shape and colour, and in its clownish antics of swimming in a head down position on the reef bottom. As it comes into adulthood it loses its colour pattern of brown with large white spots and substitutes its clownish antics with more mature behaviour. As an adult the body is decorated with smaller symmetrical brown spots on a faint yellow body.

Small to medium size fishes they range in size from 10-50cm(4-23") and come from a small family of only 120 species in 18 genera in the world ocean.

Sweetlips Hangout

Sweetlips are primarily nocturnal feeders. During the day they 'hangout' in pairs or in groups beneath coral plates or small caves. At dusk they separate from their group to forage on the outer edge of the reef, vacuuming the sandy bottom with their rubbery lips, feeding on benthic invertebrates.
The mating behaviour of Sweetlips has never been conclusively recorded but it is thought to be similar to that of Groupers (*Serranidae*) and Snappers. It is assumed that they spawn in groups at night along the outer reef.

Making Pictures of Sweetlips

Generally shy, when approached during the day Sweetlips will retire deeper into their hideouts. It is easier to get closer to them at dusk when they are actively feeding. Successful pictures can be captured with 35mm to 60mm lens.

Clown Sweetlips (Juvenile)
Plectorhinchus chaetodonoidae
60mm f2.8 / Flores, Indonesia

Yellowribbon Sweetlips
Plectrohirichus polytaenia
60mm f2.8 / Bunaken, Nth. Sulawesi

SNAPPERS
(Lutjanidae)

At some point of your sojourns into the aquatic realm you will come face to face with a family member of the Snappers who, in spite of their name, is a shy and timid fish. The Blue Striped Snapper (*Lutjanus kasmira*) is one of the most prominent members of the 'snapping' family you'll encounter on a coral reef.

Recognizing a Snapper

The Snapper or Seaperch can be distinguished by its elongated profile, semi-solid body, single dorsal fin and often visible canine teeth. Medium to large fish up to 2m(6 1/2ft) in length, they are typically 'fish' shaped in many different colours. The single most distinctive characteristic to look out for is their long pointed faces, giving their heads the profile of an isosceles triangle. They have a relatively long lifespan of between 4-21 years.

Over 100 species in 17 genera, they inhabit all tropical seas but the majority of species, including the blue striped snapper, are found in the Indo-Pacific. They inhabit shallow to intermediate reef depths up to 100m(330ft) and some deeper water species can be found in depths of 500m(1650ft).

Eat and Be Eaten

Gregarious fish they tend to mill around in small to large aggregations during the day. Though they roam over a great distance, they are never too far from the shelter of a coral. At night the groups join ranks and fan out on the reef in search of food.

Active predators, snappers usually dine at night on their staple diet of smaller fish supplemented by crabs, shrimps, crustaceans and planktonic organisms.

Snappers are popular on the human dinner table but they take their revenge! They are often the cause of food poisoning as a result of harbouring a toxin called ciguatera in their skin. This is caused by their piscine diet of Surgeonfishes (*Acanthuridae*) and Parrotfishes (*Scaridae*) who eat and accumulate the causative microorganisms of algae or dead corals.

Making Little "Snapperettes'

Snappers mate at night. Prior to their spawning activities the in-shore species migrate in a group to the outer reef to select a spawning site. The group separates into smaller units consisting of males pursuing either one or more females. There is a brief pairing period where the male nuzzles the female's anal area before the groups gather and regroup. At the peak of their union, sperm and eggs are dispersed into the water column. Their pelagic eggs hatch within 24 hours.

Snapping Snappers!

Snappers never stay still unless you can briefly corner them for a picture. Stay with them for a while and watch the corridors in which they forage. Hide behind one of them and pop out to catch your snapshot. The element of surprise is the secret.

Blue-Striped Yellow Snapper
Lutjanus kasmira
60mm F2.8 / Kadavu, Fiji

Blacktail Snapper
Lutjanus fulvus
60mm F2.8 / Bunaken, Nth. Sulawesi

FUSILIERS
(Caesionidae)

The schools of small blue silvery fishes that are frequently seen around the coral reef realm are Fusiliers. Previously they were considered a subfamily of the Snappers family *(Lutjanidae)*, but with some serious contentions the new family of *Caesionidae* has now evolved as a family in its own right in the world of fishes.

Fast Identification

Fusiliers are fast swimming schooling species, with slender streamlined bodies and forked tails. They are generally small fishes but a few species reach up to 50cm(23"). Their jaws are highly protusible with a small mouth which is adapted for plucking plankton.

Typically they are of an almost fluorescent bluish and yellow colour with lines or blotches that make them easily identifiable. The Blacktip Fusiliers *(Pterocaesio Marri)* have black tips on either side of their forked tail while the Duo Tone Neon Fusilier *(Pterocaesio Tile)* is easily identifiable by its split half and half colouration of green and orange.

Fusilier Schools

Being small in size, fusiliers convene in schools for the added protection of safety in numbers. By schooling they also achieve greater energy efficiency from each other by capitalising on the vacuum in the vortex created by the fish swimming in front.

Should fusiliers sense any danger, a signal is sent through the school and it contracts into a gleaming blue mass to confuse the predator. A delinquent that ventures out of school will quickly be taught a lesson - at his peril.

Actively roaming coastal and outer reefs in the day they love to hang in the currents feeding on fast moving plankton, especially during tidal changes. When they retire for sleep in the evening amongst the safety of the coral crevices, they turn on a 'red night-light' in their belly.

There are about 20 species in 4 genera found in the Indo-Pacific tropical waters.

Young Fusiliers

Though juvenile fusiliers are almost indistinguishable from juvenile snappers, it would not be wrong to assume that fusiliers participate in schooling sex while their cousin, the snapper, enjoys spawning in small groups. However having only recently been recognised as a separate family, there are not many references on their courtship or spawning behavior.

Hanging Out for a Fusilier Picture

Hang out on the edge of coral reefs and wait for them to swim past. Remember they are fast swimmers and silvery hence your selection of film and exposure has to be 'spot on'. Generally I would use Fuji Professional D 100 ASA film and a 24mm or 60mm lens.

Blacktip Fusiliers
Pterocaesio marri
60mm f2.8 / Great Barrier Reef, Australia

Neon Fusilier
Pterocaesio tile
60 f2.8 / Bunaken, Nth. Sulawesi

Batfishes
(Ephippidae)

Batfishes are often sighted hanging motionlessly among coral outcrops or coral trees. They belong to the *Ephippidae* family, and are renowned for their extravagant finnage. The juveniles in particular, being completely different in appearance to the adults, are conspicuous by their exotic long flowing fins.

Identity of a Batfish

A graceful fish, Batfish or Spadefish are easy to recognize with their flattened appearance, circular body and elongated symmetrical dorsal and anal fins. Already of distinctive appearance, some species even have elongated pelvic fins. They are medium sized fish reaching a maximum length of 65cm(1 1/2ft). The family consists of about 17 species in 5 genera.

The transformation from juveniles to adults is dramatic. Adults are shades of brown, black and silver with thick stripes or vertical bands across the eye, body and posterior. Juveniles are darker in colour and often have a thin orange or red colour bordering their fins. Juveniles also have exaggerated long dorsal and anal fins which decrease in length as they approach adulthood.

The juvenile Teira Tall-fin Batfish (*Platax teira*) pictured opposite has almost completely assumed adult colours but still has the orange rim bordering its fins to show that it has not quite reached maturity.

Batfishes Lifestyle

Most Batfishes are seen swimming in schools in relatively shallow waters (up to 20m/70ft) in both sheltered inshore reefs and along offshore drop-offs while some prefer to inhabit deeper waters to depths of over 40m(140ft).

They are commonly found on all tropical reefs in the Indo-Pacific ocean and some of the most graceful species are from the genus *Platax*. Hanging out in schools or in small groups amongst coral trees during the day they retire into crevices and ledges for protection at night. Batfishes can be extremely friendly and curious and it is not uncommon to be surrounded by a group of the nosy fish.

The Teira Tall-fin Batfish is particularly tame and some of them can be 'domesticated' to receive a free meal by hand. Their staple diet consists of benthic invertebrates and zooplankton, and you can often find them in big schools filter feeding in fast moving currents.

PINNATE BATFISH (JUVENILE)
Platax pinnatus
60MM f2.8 / BALI, INDONESIA

HUMP-HEADED BATFISH
Platax batavianus
60MM f2.8 / GREAT BARRIER REEF, AUSTRALIA

Batfishes
(Ephippidae)

How do Batfishes......?

Though Batfishes have eluded many of us with their courtship and sexual behaviour, recent research indicates that they are relatives of Surgeonfishes *(Acanthuridae)*, and it is now assumed that their mating activities are very similar.

Spawning in pairs, they slowly spiral to the surface to shed sperm and eggs together. Hatching occurs within 24 hours (at water temperature of 27C) and the larvae remain in the planktonic layer until they are about 10mm(5/8") before settling onto the reef.

Juvenile Antics

Some juveniles, such as those of the leafy coloured Orbicular Batfish (*Platax orbicularis*), are masters of disguise using mimicry to protect themselves against predators.
By pretending to play dead on the surface, lying on their side mimicking dead leaves, the hunted become the hunters. As they drift unnoticed on the surface amongst shoals of Fryfishes, they seize an easy dinner swimming alongside. (Randall & Emery 1971).

Photographing Batfishes

The Platax batfishes are the curious ones and they often circle divers. This makes them an easy target for the camera. Batfish make good fish pictures. The best profiles are from an upward angle which exaggerates their features.
 A 20mm lens or wider is required for a group atmospheric shot, while a 60mm is recommended for portraits.

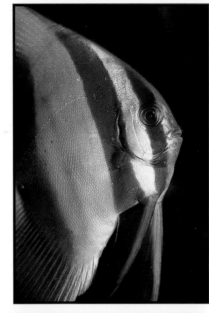

Butterflyfishes
(Chaetodontidae)

Nature has a way of putting things in perspective. Butterflyfish are not only elaborate ornaments in Neptune's garden but their abundance on a reef is a signal of the reef's fortitude and health. Often seen in groups gracefully fluttering like pieces of paper in the breeze along the reef edge, these small reef fishes with their delicate shapes, bright colours and striking patterns have also inspired many artist or designer.

Spotting a Butterflyfish

Reaching a maximum length of 30cm(1 ft) this conspicuous group of reef fishes have distinctive colour patterns. Many species has a false 'eyespot' near the tail or below the dorsal fin with a stripe or solid black bar across their real eye, presumably to help confuse predators. Along with the stripes across the body, bright yellow is the colour that features frequently in this family.

Colour patterns aside, they are easy to recognize by their physical appearance; a compressed flat disc shape, a continuous often heavily scaled dorsal fin, and in some cases a prominent elongated snout, like that of the Longnose Butterflyfish (*Forciper longirostris).*

Size and shape of their jaws differ widely to meet different dietary requirements. Many species have short jaws to nip off live coral polyps, such as the Ornate Butterflyfish *(Chaetodon ornatissimus)* of which coral polyps are its staple diet. Others like the longnose butterflyfish have elongated jaws used to pick small invertebrates from among sea urchin spines and coral crevices. A few species feed in midwater on zooplankton whilst others have a mixed diet of small invertebrates and algae. The name '*Chaetodont'* refers to the bristle like teeth possessed by all members of this family.

Family Matters

There are 120 species in 10 genera to this family, also called Coral fishes. They are found in both tropical, subtropical and warm temperate waters. The majority of butterflyfishes are located in the Indo-Pacific. Most species can be found in depths of less than 20m(66ft) though you may find some species at depths in excess of 200m(660ft).

Butterflyfishes are seen in abundance on the reef, staying close to the reef surface during the day feeding on coral polyps and zooplankton. Pyramid Butterflyfish (*Hemitaurichthys polylepis*) can be found in groups of over 200 traversing the seas of North Sulawesi. At night they seek shelter close to the reef's surface nestling in coral crevices and sponges. Being well protected, they can afford to shut down their colours for the night.

Threadfin Butterflyfish
Chaetodon auriga
60mm F2.8 / Bunaken, Nth Sulawesi

Pacific Double Saddle Butterflyfish
Chaetodon ulientensis
60mm F2.8 / Great Barrier Reef, Australia

Butterflyfishes
(Chaetodontidae)

Societies and Friends

Apart from the Chevron Butterflyfish *(Chaetodon trifasciatus)*, most butterflyfishes are easygoing placid characters, neither territorial nor aggressive. With few enemies they are often 'just there' swimming in the background. Butterflyfish society, like that of most reef fishes, is composed of a range of social units, from foraging schools to solitary home lovers. For most species, the typical social unit is a heterosexual pair that remain permanent partners.

Multiplying Butterflyfish

Generally spawning takes place at dusk and is initiated by the male after selecting his spawning territory. He courts 'his women" by swimming just in front of her fluttering his body. When she signals that she is ready by rising a little, the male then swims around her nudging her abdomen with his snout, whilst they both slowly swim towards the surface. Eggs and sperms are released simultaneously at the apex of their ascent.

Their eggs hatch in about 30 hours and unique to butterflyfishes, is their prolonged larval stage, where larvae may remain in the planktonic layer for 2-3 months before settling to the bottom as juveniles.

Making Butterflyfish Pictures

Though they are rather slow swimmers you can quickly become exhausted when chasing after a pair of butterflyfish. Start by observing them from a distance. They usually follow a set path, weaving and feeding blithesomely among corals swimming in one direction. Position yourself ahead of them and wait for them to approach and in most cases you will have a chance to fire off a few frames before they are spooked away.

Though it is easier to photograph them at night, they will have shut down their colours and pictures will look dull and uninteresting.

Longnose Butterflyfish
Forcipiger longirostris
60mm f2.8 / Aur, Malaysia

Klein's Butterflyfish(feeding)
Chaetodon kleinii
60mm f2.8 / Sipadan, Malaysia

Pyramid Butterflyfish
Hemitaurichthy polylepis
60mm f2.8 / Bali, Indonesia

ANGELFISHES
(Pomacanthidae)

Angelfishes are regarded as one of the most beautiful of all reef fishes with their brilliant colours and patterns. They have been bestowed species titles of Emperor, Regal, Queen and King Angelfish, which speak for themselves. Crowning the Neptunian reef with their ethereal presence they can hardly fail to attract the attention of any audience.

Inspecting the Royals

Close relatives of Butterflyfishes *(Chaetodontidae)*, they bear a strong resemblance in appearance sharing the compressed flat disc body shape, single long continuous dorsal and anal fins, and a small mouth with bristle-like teeth.

An Angelfish, however, can be distinguished from its first cousin fairly easily. Still small to medium sized fishes, from 7-46cm(3-20"), they tend to be larger, more brightly and luminously coloured, and have more pronounced, rough-edged scales than butterflyfishes. There are however a few small drably coloured angelfish in the genus *Centropyge*. Look out for the strong long spine at the corner of the preopercle, near the pectoral fin which is absent on butterflyfishes.

Angelfishes male's are larger than females in most genera, and colour differences exist between the sexes in the genera *Genicanthus and Chaetodontoplus*. Details vary from one species to another but generally males have stripes, are brightly coloured and have pronounced caudal fins. Females tend to be drably coloured, lack stripes and have dark upper and lower margins on the caudal fin. Colour patterns also differ between juveniles and adults.

Palatial Privacy

Approximately 80 species in 9 genera can be found in tropical and subtropical reefs. Many species inhabit shallow waters from 1-15m (3-50ft) while there are some that live in deeper waters in depths of up to 75m(250ft).

Angelfishes are dependent on the presence of shelter in the form of boulders, caves and coral crevices. Typically territorial, they spend the daylight hours near the bottom searching for food, retiring to their crevices at night. Living alone, in pairs or small groups they are shy creatures keeping their distance from divers and snorkellers. Often out of sight sheltering in a large coral head, the larger species can produce a series of noticeable loud low-frequency drumming sounds which can surprise the unwary diver.

The Gourmet Diet

Diet varies with species, from those that feed exclusively on algae or sponges supplemented by a melange of benthic invertebrates, to those that are midwater plankton feeders.

Yellowmask Angelfish
Pomacanthus xanthometopon
60mm f2.8 / Mahaheiang U/W Volcano, Nth Sulawesi

Regal Angelfish
Pygoplites diacanthus
60mm f2.8 / Bunaken, North Sulawesi

Angelfishes
(Pomacanthidae)

Uppercrust Society

The Angelfish social unit varies from couples to male-dominated harems, comprised of a small number of females. Like some other families Angelfish usually have sex reversal capabilities clearly demonstrated in their harem society.

In this instance, should the male disappear the largest dominant female will change sex and take on her old partners role, assuming that, in her Bodicea fashion, she successfully defeats the attempted coups of other neighbouring males. Within a few days she starts behaving like a male and within 3 weeks the sex reversal is complete.

Producing Royal Heirs

Spawning activity varies from genus to genus but generally occurs at dusk involving a single pair of fish. The activities are preceded by the male establishing a temporary spawning territory, typically around a prominent coral outcrop along the reef.

Territorial disputes between males may ensue over the best sites but once these have been settled the male ascends and awaits the arrival of a female. On her approach he will swim above her in full courtship display with all fins extended.

If the female is suitably impressed she ascends to join him. The pair then slowly spiral towards the surface with the male swimming around his mate and nuzzling her abdomen to heighten her arousal. Once near the surface, in a sudden orgasmic burst, eggs and sperm are released simultaneously.

Quickly over, the female heads back to the reef while the male continues to spawn as long as there are willing females present, repeatedly mating with many females that evening if he is lucky. Hatching occurs within 24 hours and the juveniles settle to the bottom when they are about three or four weeks old.

Portrait of the Royal

The royals are not really keen to grant an audience to the marine photographer. Their presence requires a royal salute to patience and dedication. Learn to catch them while they are on the move among coral heads and overhangs.

Effective strobe positioning is essential for a good portrait shot. Expose your film about 1/2-1 stop under, to bring out their royal colours.

Emperor Angelfish (Juvenile)
Pomacanthus imperator
60mm f2.8 / Similan Is, Thailand

Emperor Angelfish
Pomacanthus imperator
60mm f2.8 /
Great Barrier Reef, Australia

Damselfishes
(Pomacentridae)

The family of Damselfish is easily one of the most prolific and common groups of fish that you are likely to encounter on a reef. Darting in and out amongst corals, sponges, anemones and gorgonian fans there are over 320 species worldwide. A feature of this family apart from size is its diversity of habitat, diet, behaviour and colouration. Their popular ambassador to the world is of course the famous Clown or Anemonefish which has a separate dedication in this book.

Recognizing a Damselfish

These small fish range in size from a few centimetres to 30cm(13"). They vary immensely in colour from fluorescent blues and yellows to drab hues of grey and black.

Resembling the shape of an arrowhead, these hardy small characters can live up to the ripe old age of 10 years. Apart from shape and size other clues for identification include one continuous dorsal fin, a pronounced pelvic fin used for swimming, and moderately large scales. The caudal fin varies from triangular to forked.

Damselfishes Dwellings

While some Damselfishes, especially the Reticulated Damsel (*Dascyllus reticulatus)* and Blue Green Chromis (*Chromis viridis*), are found among hard coral, others use the entire reef as their playground, or in the case of the anemonefish (Amphiprion sp.) live exclusively with the sea anemone. Most species are found in shallow waters although some inhabit depths of up to 80m(240 ft.) (Dr G. Allen).

Active during the day, they can be seen in groups or in pairs darting in and out of their habitat. At night they take refuge amongst the protection of coral or in holes and crevices. Most Damselfishes are territorial, especially the algae eaters, defending their territory vigorously, charging at intruders regardless of their size. For the diver this can mean the occasional nip or pinch but it is nothing more than an annoyance, rarely penetrating the skin.

They are what they Eat

The Damselfish diet ranges from a variety of invertebrates, algae to zooplankton. Studies have shown that there is a correlation between staple diet and behaviour. The vegetarian algae eaters tend to be much more aggressive and territorial and generally more drably coloured, whereas many of the zooplankton feeders are more brightly coloured and timid.

The Princes Damsel
Pomacentrus vaiuli
105mm f2.8 / Flores, Indonesia

Reticaulated Damselfish
Dascyllus reticulatus
105mm f2.8 / Bunaken, Nth Sulawesi

DAMSELFISHES
(Pomacentridae)

Family Matters & Growing Pains

Damselfishes spawn in the early morning, sporadically throughout the year peaking in the summer months. For those who do not have a permanent residence (the non-territorial zooplankton eaters), pre-spawning activity includes setting up a temporary territory before courtship. In this instance the adult male selects the spawning site and prepares the nest by digging out the sand and removing algae and shells.

During this preparation period the male becomes increasingly territorial and starts courting passing females by swimming directly in front of each one in an exaggerated fashion. He then abruptly turns around in the hope of leading her back to his love nest. To attract his mating companions, the male dons a temporary exaggerated colour pattern during the mating game. The love dance is a complex one employing the use of colour, exaggerated movements and chirping sounds.

As soon as the female starts to release her eggs into the nest the male begins fertilising them. Simultaneously he circles her fiercely in order to defend the eggs from competing males. Depending on the species about 100 to 1000 eggs are released. The male then assumes a single parent role of guarding and aerating the eggs until they hatch. In some cases he spawns with several females sequentially amassing thousands of eggs in a single nest.
Eggs hatch within 2-7 days and the larvae rise to the surface to be transported by ocean currents for between 10-50 days.

Damselfish, Blennies, Gobies and Triggerfish are the few fish families that lay demersal eggs in a nest and practise parental care.

Damselfish are Impatient Models

If your selected model is not in an agitated mood then she is likely to test you to the limit by darting among the coral. The only way to catch her on film is by predicting her movements. Pre-focus your camera and, like working with a super model, fire on every move. Again the right lens is essential, generally the 105mm macro.

Golden Damsel
Amblyglyphidodon aureus
60mm f2.8 / Bunaken, Nth. Sulawesi

Green Damselfish (Juvenile)
Chromis sp.
60mm f2.8 / Phuket, Thailand

WRASSES
(Labridae)

The Wrasses are a huge family easily conspicuous by their variety and sheer abundance on the coral reef. One of their distinct and unique characteristics is the bird-like swimming action, flapping their pectoral fins just like the wings of a bird in flight.

Recognizing a Wrasse

Wrasses come in an array of shapes and sizes and vary in length from a few centimetres (Cleaner Wrasses) to the huge 2.3m(7ft) Napoleon Wrasse (*Cheilinus Undulatus*). Their diversity is like a kaleidoscope with the most complex variation of colour patterns, forms and relationships.

With such variation, their distinctive common external features are the unique beating of 'wings' style of swimming and the continuous dorsal fins. Other features to look out for in some common species are their thick lips and prominent canine teeth (buck-tooth appearance). Most wrasses are predominantly brightly coloured of composite pattern. An individualistic group, colours again vary between the gender and juveniles of each species. Within a group the dominant male is usually the most luminescent.

Habits and Habitats

During the day wrasses are found swimming on every coral reef habitat either alone, in pairs or groups. A firm believer of early to bed but late to rise, wrasses retire into holes and crevices early in the evening and they are among the last to get up in the morning. Some of the smaller species sleep in sand burrows. Happy to mind their own business they are timid creatures, non-territorial, and will tend to swim away from an approaching diver or snorkeller.

What a Varied Menu!

All members of the wrasses family are carnivorous. With their powerful teeth and jaws they feed on an extensive menu of worms, crustaceans, small molluscs, sea urchins and coral polyps. Whilst some prefer to participate in eating frenzies feeding on zooplankton, others, like the Cleaner wrasse (e.g.*Labroides dimidiatus),* earn their meals plucking off and eating parasites and algae living off the bodies of other fish. Some wrasses are like sand sorting machines who ingest mouthfuls of sand, select the tiny animals and then reject the rest of the pile.

Sex Reversal

Sexuality is a complex issue in the Wrasses society. Sex reversal is common, but unlike the damselfish it is the female who changes sex. In most species there are 2 types of male, those who are born male and stay that way, and those who start life as a female and in later life transform into functional males (changing to a much brighter colouration in the process).

Rockmover Wrasse (Juvenile)
Novaculichthys taeniourus
105mm f2.8 / Flores, Indonesia

Rockmover Wrasse (Adult)
Novaculichthys taeniourus
60mm/ f2.8 Nain, Nth. Sulawesi

WRASSES
(Labridae)

Why sex reversal occurs is not clear, although a number of factors have been suggested. One stimulus for the sex change that has been given is the correlation between males and social dominance, or more specifically simply a matter of size (Thresher 1980). The cleanerwrasse (Labroides dimidiatus) is a prime example of the male/social dominance factor where a large male dominates a harem of upto 6 females. This harem is in itself composed of a strict hierarchy with the largest female holding the highest rank of principal concubine. This role affords her enormous power over the rest of the concubines, the only one being able to cohabit the male's territory whilst being responsible for dominating the lower ranks of concubines. If the largest or any one of the females are removed, each wrasse advances one position up the social ladder.

If the male is removed, the largest female involves herself in a power struggle against neighbouring males who will attempt to take control of the territory and harem. If the female is large and aggressive enough to resist such coups, within a few hours she begins to assume the role and behaviour of a male and completes the physical change within a few days.

The Mating Game

Spawning occurs throughout the year on the edge or outer slope of a reef. Within this large family, and even within each specie, spawning occurs both in groups and in pairs.

For those wrasses that spawn in a group, the group size may consist of only a few to hundreds of fish. Spawning activity will commence with the fish slowly milling together to form a group. As the size of the group increases they swim faster and faster and more erratically, tightening up to form a very close-knit ball. At the height of the frenzy the whole group ascends into the water column then abruptly reverses direction leaving a mass of eggs and sperm behind which is soon dispersed into the current.

With the pair spawning wrasse, the male sets up a temporary spawning territory on a prominent piece of coral or rock. From here he courts passing females, looping up and down in the water column and vibrating his body whilst swimming back and forth over a prospective mate. When she is ready the female signals to the courting male by arching her body in an 'S' shape proudly displaying her egg-laden belly. They then spawn in a rapid up and down dash to the surface. Spawning only takes place during a brief period each day depending on the local conditions. In areas with strong tidal currents spawning occurs just after peak high tide, ideal for transporting eggs off the reef.

Photographing Wrasses

The bottom line is, you must have the right photographic equipment for the job. Cameras fitted with 105mm, 60mm ,to 35mm lenses are generally useful. Unless you like fish tails, do not try to out swim even an unassuming slow moving wrasse. Ascend a few meters off the reef bottom and observe their feeding ground. Select a site and wait, yes, patience is required and in most instances the wrasse will return to pick on morsels.

BLUNT HEAD WRASSE
GROUP SPAWNING SEQUENCE
Thalassoma amblycephalum
105mm f2.8 / BUNAKEN, Nth SULAWESI

BLACK BELT HOG WRASSE
Bodianus mesothorax.
60mm/ f2.8 Ambon, Indonesia

SNEAKY WRASSE
Pteragogus sp.
105mm/ f2.8 / MALDIVES

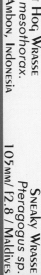

Parrotfishes
(Scaridae)

The coral reef equivalent of the terrestrial Parrot is commonly known as the Parrotfish *(Scaridae)*. They are just as brightly coloured and are equipped with beak-like jaws of fused teeth similar to their terra firma equivalent. It is their 'beak shaped' mouth and their eating habits that makes them a major contributor of sediment to beaches and coral reefs.

Parrotfish Features

With over 60 recognised species parrotfishes look very similar to wrasses in body shape and colour pattern but they are distinguished by their heavy body and beak of fused teeth. A medium to large fish they reach upto 2m(6ft) in length (Humphead Parrot fish, *Bolbometopon muricatum*) with varying colour patterns. These range from drab browns and blacks (typically of juveniles and females) to complex and brilliant combinations of red, green and blue of the larger males.

Like their close relative, Wrasses *(Labridae)*, Parrotfish have a continuous dorsal fin, relatively large scales and swim in the same bird-like fashion, flapping their pectoral fins.

Where Parrotfish 'Hangout'.

Parrotfish are typically seen browsing in groups of varying size across the coral reef. They also roam individually, while the juveniles of some species live a solitary and secret existence. Active during the day, at night they sleep in small caves, beneath ledges and under rocks. Some species protect themselves by building a mucous cocoon around themselves at night. It takes them about 30 minutes to form the transparent sac and just about as long in the morning to discard it.

Parrotfish society is composed of both nomadic species that wander in large foraging groups around a consistent part of the reef in a different area each day, and those that establish permanent territories on the reef. The wanderers are generally passive, unlike the permanent residents who are territorial in comparison. Having an established home to protect, each territory has one single male and one large dominant female with several sub-ordinate females. (See Wrasse Family, *Labridae*)

Birdseed or Fishfeed?

Parrotfish are herbivores using their strong beak jaws to scrape algae off dead corals and rocks. Some species feed on live coral. They not only consume vast quantities of algae, but in the process pick up pieces of accompanying rock and coral and pulverize them in their jaws. To make their meal digestible, they further grind the algae and rocks to sand, before filtering through the goodies and returning the leftover sediment to the reef.

Parrotfish Reproduction (Refer to Wrasse Family, Labridae)

Making Parrotfish Pictures

Parrotfishes make beautiful models. Up close at night their colours stand forth as if they have put on stage make-up for a theatrical performance. Locate them during the night sleeping in crevices and you can be assured of a brilliant portrait. In the day, catch them if you can!

Sleeping Yellowface Parrotfish
Scarus sp.
60mm f2.8 / Siau, Tioman, Malaysia

Bridged Parrotfish being service by cleanerfish
Scarus frenatus
60mm f2.8 / Bunaken, Nth Sulawesi

Filefishes
(Monacanthidae)

Filefishes are the closest relative of the Triggerfish *(Balistidae)* and they are often mistaken for one another. Filefishes would not be amused as they are a more diverse lot and in the fish world they would regard themselves as intellectually superior to their cousin with their chameleonic skills.

File Identity

Filefishes appear to be similar to triggerfishes with their compressed bodies and strong upright first dorsal spines which can be used to wedge themselves into coral crevices. However, the body of a filefish is generally more compressed with a pointed snout and they have fewer chisel-like incisor teeth.

Filefishes are referred to as Leatherjackets in Australia because of their tough leathery skin. They have the ability to change the colour of this tough skin to blend into their habitat and in some species additional tassels and appendages are developed to provide additional camouflage.

The diversity in the size and shape of filefishes varies enormously. The tiny Diamond Filefish *(Rudarius excelsus)* is only 2.5cm(1") long whilst the beautiful greenish coloured Scribble Filefish *(Aluterus scriptus)* is 1m(45") long and has a triggerfish shape.

There is also the Mimic Filefish *(Paraluteres prionurus)* who fools its predator by mimicking the colour and shape of the poisonous Black Saddled Pufferfish *(Canthigaster valentini)*. With the exception of the missing dorsal spine in the latter, both the fishes are almost identical in shape and colour pattern.

Family Affairs downunder

Filefishes are small to medium sized fish and 65 of the family, of about 80 species, can be found in the cooler Australian waters. The coral reef species lead a secretive life hiding among gorgonian fans, sea grass and *Acopora* corals. In the day they can be found alone, in pairs or in schools foraging the reef to satisfy their omnivorous diet. They feed on a great variety of food from benthic animals to plant life.

The Longnose Coral Filefish *(Oxymonacanthus longirostris)* with yellow polka dots on a light blue body is almost exclusively found in pairs wandering among hard coral plates. They are assumed to be monogamous and they are one of the most beautiful ornamental reef fishes.

Spawning is assumed to be similar to that of the triggerfish, laying demersal eggs. Please refer to the Triggerfishes *(Balistidae)* section of this book.

Pictures for the File

Most Filefishes are slow swimmers but the problem is that they are always hiding among sea grass or deep inside coral crevices. I adopt the 'lucky shot' attitude when taking pictures of them. The key to success is lots of bottom time, lots of film and of course using the right lens.

LONGNOSE CORAL FILE FISH
Oxymonacanthus longirostris
60mm f2.8 / GREAT BARRIER REEF, AUSTRALIA

Scribbled Filefish
Aluterus scriptus
60mm f2.8 / FLORES, INDONESIA

Triggerfishes
(Balistidae)

Triggerfish are definitely one of the most distinctive and highly evolved fish that live on coral reefs; they are the cousins of Filefishes *(Monacanthidae)*, Porcupinefishes *(Diodontidae)*, Boxfishes *(Ostraciidae)* and Puffers *(Tetraodontidae)*.

Often seen cruising blithesomely along the reef, the Triggerfish derives its name from the ability to lock its first dorsal fin in an erect position when wedging itself in holes, snout first. The second spine acts like the trigger of a hand gun; when depressed it releases the cocked position of the first spine.

Triggerfish Features

Closely related to Filefishes the Triggerfish family consists of 7 genera and about 35 species, many of which have complex patterns. They are recognizable by their oval platter shape, small eyes set high on the head, and small beaky mouths with long chisel-like teeth resembling that of a rabbit.

Triggerfishes are large heavy bodied fish, growing up to 75cm(30") in some of the larger species. The 2nd dorsal fin and anal fins are almost identical in size which gives a side-profile appearance of only two recognizable fins on each side of the body. They use these fins for swimming. Their tail fins is put into operation only when speed or quick evasive action are required.

A Shy and Retiring Character

Triggerfishes are reef dwellers and generally tend to be solitary creatures found throughout the Indo-Pacific. Most of the smaller species are shy, especially the Luminous Blue Triggerfish *(Odonus niger)*, which will usually dive for cover when approached by a diver. When evading predators, they will use their trigger mechanism to wedge themselves tightly in holes and crevices until the danger has passed. For a safe nights' sleep Triggerfish are found adopting the same pose, with only their tail hanging out of small holes.

Brooding and Breeding in the Harem

In contrast to most other fishes who disperse their eggs in the open sea, Triggerfish are one of the few fish families who practice parental care. Recent research has shown that in contrast to other families that practise parental care (Blennies, Damselfishes and Gobies) in which the male guards the demersal eggs, it is the female Triggerfish who assumes the protective maternal role (Frick 1980).

Nests are usually shallow craters between 50-80cm(20-30") in diameter found in the sand or rubble. The nest site is dug out by the female by ejecting jets of water from her mouth to clear the sand and then removing rubble with her jaws.

Spawning takes place before dawn after a brief courtship with the male swimming between the nest site and the female sleeping quarters. The eggs are laid in the nest and fertilized in a concentrated mass. The female then guards them until they hatch. With an incubation period of less than 24 hours the female Triggerfish has a better deal in comparison to other fish families that practise parental care. Juvenile triggerfishes are not as brilliantly coloured as the adults.

Titan Triggerfish~ after lunch
Balistodes viridescens
60mm f2.8 / Bunaken, Nth. Sulawesi

Titan Triggerfish~ guarding nest site
Balistodes viridescens
60mm f2.8 / Makalahe, Nth. Sulawesi

TRIGGERFISHES
(Balistidae)

When Jekyll turns into Hyde

Most of us are well informed of hazardous marine animals, but the average person is unaware that the Triggerfish should be added to the list. When an intruder approaches the vicinity of their offspring, these normally passive fish turn violent. The cause of this spontaneous act of aggression is that the fish, invariably the female, is protecting her eggs. This aggressive behaviour is not reserved simply for other fish, that try and eat their eggs, but is also extended to any unwary diver that approaches her nest. Often this behaviour just consists of a darting quick movement towards the intruder, followed by a quick retreat back to the nest.

There have been many reports of divers that have actually been attacked, including the authors themselves. I experienced an attack by a Titan Triggerfish (*Balistoides viridescens*) on a wall dive off Bunaken Island in North Sulawesi. I had been aware of a Triggerfish swimming parallel with us for a short distance when suddenly I looked down to see the 70cm(32") size fish, rushing at me teeth protruding. Swimming to catch Michael's attention a few feet away we fended off our attacker by pushing it away with our fins.

Like a fighter-plane engaged in a dog-fight, the persistent blighter charged at us from various directions. After repeated attempts, the fish withdrew without any injury sustained to either party. Reported attacks have not resulted in any fatal injury, but Triggerfish are capable of inflicting huge bruises and severe lacerations removing small chunks of flesh which require surgical stitches.

Some of the bigger species of Triggerfish have a bad reputation, namely the Yellow-spotted (*Pseudobalistes fuscus*) and the Titan Triggerfish, and it is recommended that divers should grant them their due respect. If a large stationary fish is facing you directly in your path of travel, alter course to avoid confrontation. This could be a female guarding her nest.

What's on the Menu?

Feeding on a wide variety of marine animals the Triggerfish uses its powerful jaws and teeth to crunch hard shelled species such as crabs, sea urchins, molluscs and even coral into little digestible pieces. Each jaw is equipped with the ideal crunching and munching tools with 8 long protruding incisors in an outer row buttressed by a secondary inner row of 6 teeth.

Be Trigger Happy when Shooting Triggerfish!

It is pretty hard to shoot a good picture of a Triggerfish. You will find them wedged into small crevices, out of range, or descending on you so that you'll be too busy fending them off with your cameras. If you do find one that co-operates, make sure you finish the roll off! I got lucky with one that was busy at lunch with a Spanish dancer nudibranch and expended a whole roll of film on a very content Triggerfish.

Clown Trigger-fish
Balistodes viridescens
24mm f2.8 / Chumpon, Thailand

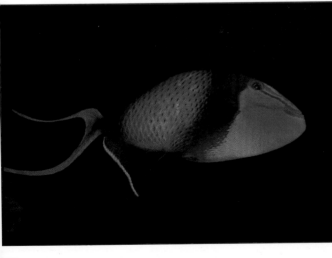

Mid-night Blue Tiggerfish
Odonus niger
60mm f2.8 / Ruang, Nth. Sulawesi

Surgeonfishes
(Acanthuridae)

Surgeonfishes are the gregarious and gentle but intrepid inhabitants of the coral reef. Of distinctive features, they are characterized by the presence of a razor sharp spine on both sides of the caudal peduncle (base section of the tail area). Referred to as the 'scalpel', it is this spine which gives the family its common surgical name.

Recognising a Surgeonfish

Surgeonfishes can be identified by their flat typically oval, sometimes circular, side profile enhanced by the continuous even dorsal and anal fins. Drab or brightly coloured they are medium to large sized solid fish ranging from 20-100cm(9-45"). Their small eyes are positioned high on their rounded head and they have conspicuous small mouths with incisor-like teeth suited to nibbling or scraping algae and plants from rocks or corals.

For self defence, all Surgeonfishes carry a retractable spine or spines on their caudal peduncle which may not be noticeable at a first glance.(See picture opposite)

The 72 species of this family have been classified into 3 subfamilies; *Acanthurinae, Nasinae, and Prionurinae.* The *Acanthurinae* is the largest subfamily with 36 species of which the Blue Striped Surgeonfish *(Acanthurus lineatus)* has a single venomous spine at the base of the tail area. Another subfamily *Nasinae,* or Unicornfish, are equipped with one or two hook-like spines on either side of the tail base and they are easily distinguishable by the hump or unicorn horn protruding from their forehead. The females of some species have a much smaller horn, some have none at all. Sightings of the third subfamily *Prionurinae* are rare but they are recognisable by their multiple bony tail plates.

Homes and Habits of Surgeonfishes

Mostly found in small groups or in shoals in the tropical waters of Indo-Pacific reefs, they are typically seen in the day swimming in shallow waters of around 2m(7ft), although some species are found traversing at depths of 100m(330ft). At night they sleep alone in coral crevices.

Generally unassuming and timid, swimming away on your approach, they only use the spiny scalpel in defence against predators, and as an offensive weapon when engaged in combat with other fish. With a quick sweep of their tail, they are capable of fatally slashing other fish or causing serious lacerations to humans who manhandle them. In combat the fish warily circle their enemy with their spine angled towards them.

Surgical sharp spine of a Blue Striped Surgeonfish
Acanthurus lineatus
60mm f2.8 / Bunaken, Nth. Sulawesi

Vlaming's Unicornfish
Naso vlamingii
60mm f2.8 / Great Barrier Reef, Australia

Surgeonfishes
(Acanthuridae)

The Marine Vegetarians

Whilst most fishes are typically predator, Surgeonfishes are one of the few exceptions. They are mainly herbivores that often graze on the plentiful supplies of algae on the reef. Some Surgeonfishes have especially adapted digestive tracts that allow them to ingest sand whilst feeding, extracting the nutrients, and then excreting the waste. Scraping rocks or the coral surface also provides a varied diet. Unicornfishes are an exception to their 'vegetarian' equivalents typically feeding in large aggregates on zooplankton.

Surgeoning Sexual Behavior

Surgeonfishes courting and spawning activities are similar to many of their counterparts, where pelagic eggs are typically produced in the water column after a short spawning ascent. Spawning usually takes place at dusk either between individual pairs and/or groups spawning in a single unit.

The male initiates the affair by approaching the female and swimming by her side for a period before the pair take off slowly in unison into the water column to an explosion of sperm and eggs. The male often assumes temporary colour patterns for courtship. The mating sequence of the surgeonfish is at a much slower pace compared to the frantic orgasmic dashed by other fishes.

Group spawning for surgeonfishes is very similar to that described for wrasses (Labridae) and parrotfish (Scaridae). Prior to spawning the group gathers along the outer edge of the reef flirting with each other whilst gradually forming tighter groups. Eventually in response to some unseen signal they dash to the surface in parallel formation and at the apex of their ascent shed eggs and sperm. Spawning ascents often occur throughout the school simultaneously which is an impressive sight to see. Hatching occurs typically just over 24 hours later, with the larvae being found well offshore. They have a long planktonic stage of a few months before full adolescence is reached.

Pictures of Surgeonfishes

Surgeonfishes found alone or in small groups have erratic swimming movements while the schooling type are fast swimmers. These make life rather difficult for the photographer. Locate their feeding ground and catch them feeding from a distance of 2m(7ft) or find them at night for close up portraits. The 60mm macro lens is highly recommended. My favourites are the fluorescent Blue Striped Surgeonfish (Acanthurus lineatus) and the Blue Surgeonfish (Paracanthurus hepatus) with the shape of a number 6 on its lumier body

Spotted Surgeonfish
Naso brevirostris
60mm f2.8 / Bunaken, Nth. Sulawesi

Number 6 Palette Surgeonfishes
Paracanthus hepatus
60mm f2.8 / Maldives

Moorish Idol
(Zanclidae)

Looking much like a bandit in daylight, the Moorish Idol (*Zanclus cornutus*) is one of the most prominent and frequently seen fish members of the coral reef community. Its distinctively flowing extended dorsal fin, bright yellow and white colours and black stripes will quickly capture the attention of any reef watcher. There could be no other smaller fish family than the Moorish idol which consists of only one species. Its popularity among divers and snorkellers have earned it a special place in this book.

An often Mistaken Idol

The Moorish idols' extremely long flowing and filamentous third dorsal spine arising from its back, has caused it to be mistaken for the Common and Schooling Bannerfishes *(Heniochus acuminatus and Heniochus diphreutes)* which also don similar extended dorsal fins.

On careful observation, however, the Moorish idol is distinctly different to the bannerfishes in its strongly pointed long snout with a yellow bridge and its black bar colouring. Two black vertical bars flow from the nape to the abdomen and a second bar through the rear dorsal and anal fins (see picture opposite). An adult Moorish idol is also identified by a small bony projection in front of the eyes.

Being a close relative of the Surgeonfish (*Acanthuridae*) they inherit a deep strongly compressed body, giving a flat profile, with equal sized dorsal and anal fins.

Often found in pairs or small groups in the shallow waters of a coral reef they have been reported to venture into the abyssal depths of over 180m(600ft). Though omnivorous feeders, they prefer to pick on scrumptious sponges and coral bits rather than boring green algae.

Sex Idol

Although it is one of the most common fish seen by divers, amazingly there have been no reports of any courtship or spawning activities of the Moorish idol. Scientists are certain that they spawn at dusk and it is known that they produce pelagic eggs. Often observed in twosomes in the late afternoon this might suggest that they spawn in pairs rather than being group sex participants.

Idol Pictures

The Moorish idol is not camera shy. Although frequently on the move, snap shots of this all time favorite fish can easily be captured with a 60mm lens. Group shots can be taken with a 24mm-35mm lens.

Moorish Idol
Zanclus cornutus
60mm f2.8 / Bunaken, Nth. Sulawesi

Moorish Idols
Zanclus cornutus
20mm f2.8 / Similan, Thailand

BARRACUdAS
(Sphyraenidae)

Swimming amongst a school of Barracuda in the blue water is an awesome experience. Among the top predators of the ocean, their sleek elongated, cylindrical, silvery bodies resemble small torpedoes. Barracudas belong to the single genus *Sphyraenidae* family with only 20 species, and are only found in the tropical seas of the world.

Fearsome Appearance

People who describe barracudas as the meanest critters on the reef are perhaps intimidated by their pointed snouts and protruding lower jaws. Their large mouth are filled with an awesome array of long scissor sharp teeth. With small fins and a forked tails, their silvery elongated bodies with dark bars or chevron markings radiate an aura of a vicious predator. Medium to large fish they can reach up to 2m(6.6ft) in length.

Some large species of barracudas (*Sphyraena barracuda*), if encountered alone, have a habit of approaching a diver at close range out of curiosity. Despite looking fierce they are generally harmless as their diet consists primarily of fish and the occasional treat of sea jellies. However, have due respect for barracudas, as they have been known to snap hand spears in half and bite through propeller blades!

Schooling Advantage

Young barracudas believe strongly in safety in numbers and schooling for survival. We would often find them hanging out at the outer edge of a reef, and sometimes the school was so enormous that it was like swimming through a solid curtain of silver. They look like precision swimming machines moving in exact co-ordination, exactly the same speed and distance from each other. If danger is detected by any member of the school, the slightest change in direction will cause an immediate chain reaction throughout the whole school.

We once observed an Oceanic Whitetip shark (*Carcharhinus longimanus*) trying to pluck the last swimming member of a school of barracuda. The entire school immediately changed direction to face the shark and at the same time closed ranks and contracted to form one big silvery mass. The shark turned on its fins and frantically disappeared into the ocean realm.

Though little is known about barracudas' courtship or spawning affairs, they are generally assumed to migrate to a specific spawning site in large groups (Johannes 1981). Mating in schools has advantages, as the close physical proximity of males and females makes fertilization of eggs more efficient. In some species (*Sphyraena barracuda*), fully mature adults leave the school, returning only for mating.

Barracuda Pictures are Always in Demand

The problem is having the right lens at the right time. Usually you can slowly merge into a school of barracuda which is a wild and adrenalin pumping experience. Due to reflection from their silvery body, shut down your strobe to 1/2 power and aim for the sky. A 15mm lens is recommended.

CHEVRON BARRACUDA
Sphyraena putnamiae
24mm f2.8 / Bunaken, Nth. Sulawesi

GREAT BARRACUDA
Sphyraenis barracuda
60mm F2.8 / Ruang, Nth Sulawesi

Sharks

The mention of the word shark is enough to send shivers running down the spines of most people. Myths, superstition, and the movies have ensured that the public retains the image of a shark as a man-eating, ferocious and savage predator. Although shark attacks are real, only a few species are known to attack humans under ambiguous circumstances. These incidents are few and far between and, out of the 350 species, only a few species are known to have caused injury.

Recognising Sharks

Everyone is familiar with the shape of the shark. Shape and size varies for each species as does their habitat and mode of sociability. They are however typically cigar shaped in shades of grey and silver with long pointed elongated snouts, a pair of obvious nostrils, numerous sharp conspicuous teeth, large pectoral fins and that infamous pointed upright dorsal fin or fins.

Sharks have coarse denticles instead of scales and their skeletons are made of cartilage instead of bone.

Nature's Garbage Removers

Sharks are flesh eaters and nocturnal hunters feeding mainly on fishes, crustaceans and molluscs. Contrary to popular belief however, it is not human flesh that forms part of their diet. They possess good eyesight, an excellent sense of smell and a good sets of teeth, often with serrated teeth, in the fish-eating species, designed for seizing and tearing their prey. They also have the finely tuned ability to detect low frequency vibrations at considerable distances. This enables detection of prey from a distance (the electric field surrounding a sleeping or sick fish, for instance), and in turn acts as an early warning system against predators.

Sharks are the "garbage removers of the sea". The duties assigned to them are to remove sick fishes which would otherwise spread disease among the rest of the reef community.

Research has shown that a human swimming on the surface emits the same energy signals as a sick fish, hence unprovoked attacks on humans happen at or near the surface, a case of mistaken identity by sharks trying to do their job.

Different Reproductive Characteristics

Sharks differ from other fishes in their method of reproduction. Firstly, shark's eggs are fertilized internally. After a rough courtship for the female, who is often repeatedly bitten by the male prior to copulation, sexual intercourse involves the male inserting his clasper (a two penis-like appendage) into the female's genital organ.

Blackrip Reef Shark
Carcharhinus melanopterus
60mm f2.8 / Bunaken, Nth. Sulawesi

Tawny Reef Shark
Nebrius ferrugineus
20mm f2.8 / Burmease Bank

Sharks

A shark's pregnancy period varies as does the method of gestation. The duration ranges from a few months to a few years. Most mothers carry the developing embryos in their uterus, like in humans, and produce live young. In a few species however, like the Swell *(Scyliorhinidae sp.)*, Horn and Port Jackson (Heterodon*tus* sp.) sharks, the embryos are sealed in leathery egg cases and deposited on the bottom.

Sharks also differ in the number of young they bear. Most fish lay pelagic eggs in vast numbers which have a low survival rate. In contrast sharks bear only a few young, called pups, but at birth they are fully developed and equipped for survival with the ability to swim and hunt on their own. In some 'Advanced' shark families, to guarantee survival after birth, the fittest pup actually devours the weaker ones while still in the womb of its mother. Sharks are said to be far superior to humans in this instance.

Reef Sharks

Reef sharks that you are most likely to see swimming around the outer reefs or resting beneath ledges or in caves are the Blacktip (*Carcharodon melanopterus*), Reef Whitetip (*Triaendon obesus)*, Leopard shark *(Stegostoma fasciatum)* and Nurse shark *(Gynglymostomatidae).*

The Blacktip shark and Reef Whitetip shark are easily identified by their respective black or white tip on the dorsal, caudal, pelvic and pectoral fins. Both feed mainly on fishes but supplement their diet with crustaceans and are considered harmless. The Blacktip shark an active swimmer, reaches a length of 2.5m(8ft) whilst the more slender Whitetip reaches a maximum size of 2.1m(7ft) and tends to be more curious often approaching divers at close range. Both have small litters of about 10 pups.

The Leopard shark, so called because of its spots, has one large and one small dorsal fin, and an extremely long rounded caudal fin. Grey to yellow brown with spots with a common size of 150-250cm(5-8ft) they are sluggish slow swimmers are considered harmless.

Nurse sharks can be recognised by their two equal-sized dorsal fins and barbels on the chin (whiskers) and can often be seen cruising around the bottom in search of food, with their mouth and barbels close to the ground. Their diet includes mainly fishes, crabs, lobsters, and other crustaceans. They are generally considered to be harmless but if provoked may bite and inflict serious injury.

Shark Pictures

It is not easy to see a shark, let alone photograph one. Most good shark photographs are taken during shark feeds. This practise however may alter their natural behavior and cause feeding frenzies that can result in injuries to both sharks and photographer.

The best opportunity to photograph sharks without provoking them is on the outer reef, where they are frequently seen cruising the reef or found resting beneath ledges or in crevices.

Leopard Shark
Stegostoma fasciatum
20mm f2.8 / Semilan Is, Thailand

White Tip Reef Shark
Trianodon obesus
14mm f3.5/ Banka Is, Nth. Sulawesi

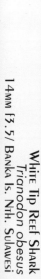

FISHES ARE OUR CONNECTION
TO THE SECRETS OF THE SEA

(ma)

The Bottom Dwellers

Fishes
usually found
Living on the reef flat
reef wall, or sea bed

Lizardfishes
(Synodontidae)

The appearance of Lizardfishes reminds us of ancient animals from the Jurassic era. Possessing a reptile-like head with a fearsome personality to match, they are ferocious predators endowed with a large mouth and numerous sharp teeth. Even their tongue is lined with inward directed teeth. Sitting patiently on the reef they are well camouflaged by their body colouration, silently poised waiting for potential prey.

Distinctly Reptilian

Their reptilian-like head gives a side profile similar to that of the terra-firma lizard from where their name is derived. Their almost cigar-shaped body is cylindrical, moderately elongated and all their fins are spineless. A high dorsal fin is situated along the mid-body, followed by barely visible small fins and forked caudal fins.

Despite their primitive features of rounded scales and abdominal pelvic fins, some species have surprisingly advanced features such as the buoyancy control of a swim bladder. Their body colours match their particular habitat and provide excellent camouflage, typically silvery sandy grey colours although they are often bright red in deep water.

The Lizardfish family consists of about 40 known species in 3 genera. The largest species measure up to 60cms(27inches) and some species live at a depth of up to 400m(1320ft), although most live in the shallower waters of the reef.

Lizardfish Country

Living alone in the sparse open sedimentary reef bottom, Lizardfishes have the ability to quickly bury themselves completely in the sandy bottom, leaving only their eyes peeping out to scan for unsuspecting prey.

All Lizardfishes are ravenous carnivores employing cryptic antics to catch their prey. Capable of darting upward in a flash to feed on small fishes they gulp and swallow the fish whole. On a few occasions they have been observed prolonging the timing of their darting technique for the worthier prize of a larger Butterflyfish (*Chaetodontidae)* for dinner.

Javelin Lizardfish
Synodus jaculum
105mm f2.8 / Bunaken, Nth Sulawesi

Clearfins Lizardfish
Synodus dermatogerys
105mm f2.8 / Bunaken, Nth Sulawesi

Lizardfishes
(Synodontidae)

Eat and be Eaten!

We had a unique experience watching a Javelin Lizardfish *(Synodus jaculum)* successfully leap up about 1m(3ft) to catch a 3cm(1 1/2") Sabretooth Bluestriped Blenny *(Plagiotremus rhinorhynchos)* in mid-water for lunch. Settling to the bottom the blenny was swallowed whole in 3 gulps.

The next moment, a soul mate of the ill-fated blenny took revenge by latching on to the underside of the lizardfish's jaw with its fangs. The fearsome predator, who had now turned prey, was next seen swimming frantically to shake the attacker off its jaw. The bold blenny eventually detached itself but only after it had successfully reeked revenge and a huge chunk of tissue off its victim.

Old Fashioned Courtship

Lizardfishes indulge in prolonged courtship before spawning with their partner. Courtship occurs throughout the day with the male actively pursuing a female companion. Whenever she stops, he will attempt to sit in front of her with gills fully flared showing his courtship colours. Sometimes he can be seen sitting side by side or across her.

Once she has submitted to his persistent pursuit, the pair can be seen making lengthy and elaborate movements along the reef flat. The male will stay and defend her until she is ready to spawn.

Spawning occurs at dusk, with the pair ascending about 5m(16.5ft) off the bottom simultaneously to eject clouds of elongated pelagic eggs, which take about 3-4 days to develop into skinny larva.

Easy Targets for Fish Photographers

Taking pictures of a fish has never been easier. Lizardfishes sit still whilst having their portrait taken. Both night and day you can locate them in their open reef habitat and all you have to do is just settle down gently in front of them to start your photo session. Making pictures of them during mating season or feeding time is a real test of patience.

Variecated Lizardfish
Synodus variegatus
60mm f2.8 / Bunaken, Nth Sulawesi

Javelin Lizardfish
Synodus jaculum
60mm f2.8 / Flores, Indonesia

Scorpionfishes
(Scorpaenidae)

If anything in the fish world was to be compared to a creature from outer space it would have to be from the diverse and bizarre family of *Scorpaenidae*. The beauties and beasts of the reef, they range from the reds and flamboyant spiked wings of Firefishes (*Pterois*), to the ogreish grumpy face and monstrous appearance of Stonefishes (*Synanceia*).

The Adams Family

Small to medium size heavy bodied fish they are usually less than 30cm(12in) in length. A family of diverse appearance from the huge ornate pectoral 'wings' of the commonly observed Lionfishes (*Dendrochirus*) and firefishes, to the dull mottled warty stonefishes. For this reason they have been divided into a number of sub-families, and have been given many common names such as Zebrafish, Turkeyfish, Butterflycod, and Waspfish, all evoking images of either danger or beauty.

Scorpionfishes get their name from their venomous spines. In some species they are more conspicuous than others, like the highly manoeuvrable spines of the dorsal fin of lionfishes. They have relatively large heads and large pectoral fins which are more like wings or fans. Lionfishes have high cheekbones with a few spines, toady mouths and bulbous eyes set high on the head.

Colour patterns vary from the bright reds, oranges, stripes and ornate plumage of the lionfishes, to the well camouflaged drab mottled hues of brown and green of the stonefishes. Some species in the *Scorpaenopsis* genus have additional leafy tassels, warts and bumps on their body coverings, and would certainly win no beauty contest. They are all artists of disguise. By growing additional appendages or producing mucus to stick bits of algae on to their bodies and then laying semi-buried in silt, they are perfectly camouflaged from both their predators and prey.
The Scorpionfish family comprise of approximately 350 species in 70 genera and are found mostly in Indo-Pacific waters.

Poisonous Prickles

All scorpionfishes have potentially dangerous venomous spines positioned on their dorsal fins (sometimes also on anal and pectoral fins). Under normal conditions they lay flat on the back and are raised only as a defence mechanism when the fish is disturbed or harassed.

Each spine is like a hypodermic needle connected to a venom sac at the base of the dorsal fin and ejects highly toxic venom into the intruder. The message simply is "Do not touch me!".

Ragged-finned Firefish
Pterois antennata
60mm f2.8 / GREAT BARRIER REEF, AUSTRALIA

Bearded Scorpion-Fish
Scorpaenopsis cirrhosa
60mm f2.8 / MANADO, NTH SULAWESI

Injuries can vary from like that of a bee-sting, to throbbing, or repeating waves of excruciating pain. A wound from the deadly stonefish can result in paralysis, convulsions, unconsciousness, even cardiac and respiratory failure.

All scorpionfishes are not aggressive. The onus is on the victim who might accidently step on, or press their hand on to a poor fish taking a nap on the reef bed. All scorpionfishes wounds should be immediately immersed in hot water (as hot as you can stand). This will help alleviate the pain and inactivate the toxin.

Ambush, Pounce and Pray

Scorpionfishes are solitary nocturnal predators that feed on crustaceans and small fishes. They lie on the reef bed or in caves and under ledges, and are typically found in depths of 2-30m(6-100ft). While Lionfishes are slightly more active at night roaming the reef in search of food, most scorpionfishes remain almost stationary.

They employ ambush and decoy techniques to fish for dinner. Sitting patiently and motionlessly, they can take off at the speed of light to engulf passing fishes or crustaceans. We once witnessed a lionfish pounce by swiftly performing a 180 degree turn to swallow a moving basslet (*Anthiinae*).
Some species are opportunistic feeders. Sitting camouflaged on the bottom they will sometimes engulf an innocent by-stander for an easy dinner.

Mating with the Scorpionfish

Scorpionfishes' courtship begins after twilight. To win his mate for the evening the male sometimes has to engage in a brawl of head ramming with other potential suitors. Once successful he will don his courtship robe and patrol his territory for a female companion.

When a female enters his courtyard, he swims and circles her, slowly positioning himself at her side. He then initiates the spawning by swimming a few feet off the bottom and, when fully aroused, she will join him in his ascent to the surface to shed balls of thousands of floating eggs and sperm together. While the female descends to rest for the night, the male will hang around his lair to wait for another passing female.

Portraits of Scorpionfishes

Scorpionfishes are perfect portrait subjects! Shoot them any which way you can. Approach at your own pace (they move very slowly or not at all) and select their best profiles. They tend to harbour great facial expressions with those lovely colourful tassels.

Dwarf Lionfish
Dendrochirus brachypterus
60mm f2.8 /Bitung, Sulawesi

A Scorpionfish yawning?
Scorpaenopsis sp.
60mm f2.8 / Aur, Malaysia

Leaf Scorpion-Fish
Taenianotus triacanthus
60mm f2.8/ Manado, Nth Sulawesi

GOATFISHES
(Mullidae)

Like terra firma animals ranging in the meadows, Goatfishes are often observed scavenging the reef bed for food. Their behaviour and facial expressions often reminds us of that famous Manchurian gentleman, Fu Man Chu, with his curled up whiskers.

Goatfish Features

The most obvious features of the Goatfish are a pair of "goats whiskers", otherwise called barbels, on its chin and the distinctively forked caudal fin. Other clues in the identification of this family include the two well separated dorsal fins and an elongated but solid body.

Colouration ranges from the brightly yellow striped Goatfish to the iridescent pink and blue multi-bars species. They are medium sized fish, from 20cm(9") up to 50cm(23") for the largest member of the family. A small family consisting of about sixty species there are size differences between the sexes and species type.

Goatfish Hangouts and Eateries

Though a few species of Goatfish prefer to hangout in schools, most of them are found probing along the sandy bottom of a reef individually or in small groups. Using their wriggling barbels as food detectors, they shift a lot of sand in one day in search of their carnivorous diet of worms, crustaceans and small molluscs that live in the sand.

Goatfish seem to have an insatiable appetite and bad eating habits. Pouncing sporadically upon some uncovered titbit they burrow their snouts into the sand leaving behind a cloud of sediment and crumbs. Of course other fishes like Wrasses (Labridae) take advantage of the situation trailing along behind and freeloading off the leftovers morsels.

Dash Dot Goatfish
Parupeneus barberinus
60mm f2.8 / Manado Murex Reef, North Sulawesi

Yellow Striped Goatfish
Mulloides vanicolensis
60mm f2.8 / GBR, Australia

Goatfishes
(Mullidae)

Broadminded Reproductive Behaviour

Goatfish spawn in pairs or groups at the outer edge of the reef away from their normal feeding grounds. Within the pair-spawning species, courtship behaviour is initiated by the male patiently patrolling 1-2m(3-6ft) above the reef awaiting the arrival of the female.

When she arrives she approaches the male. Immediately the brief but fervent courtship follows, with the male swimming around her in circles in an exaggerated display wriggling his barbels rapidly. When fully aroused the pair will dash to the surface together and release their gametes simultaneously.

Within the group-spawning species, the ritual begins with participating individuals from each pair approaching one another and swimming horizontally about 1m(2-3ft) off the bottom. Others then join the pair converging into a group before dashing to the surface in unison for an explosion of gametes. The climax is over in seconds and the group disperses to join the other fish below.

The floating fertilized eggs hatch after a few days but the larvae only settle to the bottom when they are between 40 and 60mm(1 1/2-2 1/2") where they develop the characteristic barbels and change into the adult colours. Adulthood is said to be attained when they reach a length of 9-10cm(3 1/2-4").

Working with a Goatfish

Goatfishes are easy to approach. They are amazing to watch and they do not mind having their picture taken even when you are observing their ill-mannered eating habits.

During the day scan the reef from about 2m(6ft) off the bottom and you will almost certainly spot a Goatfish literally sweeping the reef bed. Approach gently, and your subject will be quite oblivious of your presence and blinding effect of underwater strobes.

Some Goatfish prefer to sleep out in the open and seem to have the ability to add enhanced highlights to their bright red, pink, yellow blue colours to warn off potential predators of the night. This is a great opportunity for great portraits, where you can take your time to experiment with various camera angles and exposures.

DoubleBar Goatfish
Parupeneus bifasciatus
60mm f2.8 / Great Barrier Reef, Australia

Red Patch Goatfish
Parupeneus heptacanthus
60mm f2.8 / Ruang Island, North Sulawesi

ANEMONEFISHES
(Amphiprion & Premnas species)

The Anemonefish is so called because of its special living arrangement amongst the stinging tentacles of sea anemones. Although part of the Damselfish family its symbiotic relationship with the anemone, bright colours, and clownish antics have earned it a special place in this book as well as the common name of clownfish.

Identifying Anemonefishes

Anemonefish are easily recognizable, a common sighting, and fun to watch. They are found living in sea anemones and you will find them darting in and out of the tentacles of their host in a schizophrenic manner as if in a game of hide and seek.

Found in all tropical reefs from the Red Sea to the Central Pacific there are 27 known species in the genus of *Amphiprion*, and 1 in the genus *Premnas* which is distinguished by one or two spines in the cheek. The bright colours of Anemonefish form part of their effective defense mechanism warding off predators. Typically they feature one to three vertical white bars across the body and in two species the bars are replaced by a white stripe running along the back from head to tail.

Tenant and Landlord

Found at depths of 1-50m(2-160ft) Anemonefish typically live together in a group on a single anemone and they are rarely seen away from their host. One of the most fascinating aspects of this small fish is its immunity to the anemone's stinging cells (nematocyst), whose slightest touch would paralyze other fish. These fish are not born with an in-built immunity system. They have to acquire it by picking up a substance from the mucus coated tentacles that prevents the nematocyst from firing and the tentacles stinging each other.

A newly born fish or one that has become separated from its host anemone for too long will have to acclimatize by rubbing itself against the tentacles to coat its body with the anemone mucus. Once the gradual acclimatization is complete the anemonefish is fully immune to the sting and can spend unlimited time in the arms of its host - nature's way of ensuring a constant bond between fish and anemone.

Completely dependent on their landlord for protection, an anemonefish will disappear quickly into its safe haven upon imminent danger. Within the relationship, the anemone is clearly seen as the 'big brother' offering the fish a home, protection, and also a source of food. The benefit to the anemone is not so clear, although it is said to enjoy the housecleaning provided by the fish. A 'clownfish' is never seen without an anemone; whilst an anemone can survive quite happily on its own.

Behavioural traits

A courageous defender of their home anemonefish is territorial in behaviour, fearlessly charging the intruder regardless of their size. An agitated or ill tempered anemonefish may even ram an intruders or attack a scuba diver, or photographers' camera equipment. However the attack, will result in nothing more than a nip or a pinch of the skin.

With a life expectancy of at least 10 years they live in a social group, active during the day and sleeping at night amongst the folds of the anemone completely entangled in its tentacles.

Spine cheek Clownfish
Premnas biaculeatus
60mm f2.8 / Tioman, West Malaysia

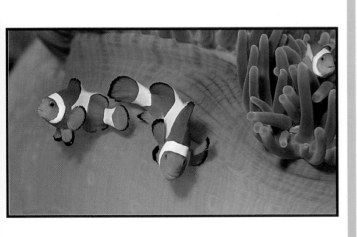

Common Clownfish
Amphiprion ocellaris
60mm f2.8 / Nain, North Sulawesi

ANEMONEfishes
(Amphiprion & Premnas species)

Food sources

Feeding on zooplankton that floats past, the anemone itself also provides the fish with an additional food source. The Anemonefish dines on the leftovers of food and algae on the anemone's tentacles and oral disc which might otherwise cause disease in its host, benefiting both host and tenant.

Who is the Boss? (Living Together and Breeding)

Anemonefish live in a hierarchical social system. This is based on size and consists of the two largest adults at the top of the social ladder, of which the female is the largest and most socially dominant followed by the largest male which is her partner for life. All other fishes within the same household are male and smaller in size. In most cases there is only one pair of adults to each anemone who permit juveniles and smaller Anemonefish to co-exist with them.

`One of the most intriguing things about the anemonefish is its ability to change sex. They are hermaphrodites. All are born male but they have the ability to transform into females when the appropriate time arrives.

If their female anemonefish disappears or dies her male partner will change sex over a couple of weeks, transforming into a female and assuming the leading role of the group. The next largest male will grow a little bigger and become her mate, with each fish advancing one place in the hierarchy. This process can be amazingly reversed should the prodigal 'big mother' decide to have a change of heart and return home.This practice is an efficient method of perpetuating their own species.

The base of an anemone is a safe haven for a nest and spawning, which takes place up to 13 times throughout the year. The courting process is initiated by the male who continuously bites at the tentacles of the anemone until they are withdrawn to reveal the nest site. The male then leads the female to his lair and after bouts of body biting the trembling female starts laying between 300-500 eggs. He then swims over and fertilizes them. It is the male who performs the parental care by fanning the eggs to provide a steady flow of oxygen-rich water and defending them until they hatch in 6-10 days. Hatching usually occurs just after sundown and the microscopic offspring then float away. After 15 days of floating and growing the tiny juvenile fish are ready to bond with a host anemone and begin the process of acclimatization.

Making Clownfish Pictures

'Clownfish' are our favorite photographic subjects, but they are not co-operative models. With lots of patience a great picture can be captured with a Nikonos and a 3:1 extension tube or a housed camera with a 60mm lens. Do not try to chase the fish all over the anemone. This may cause injury to both its host and the fish. With your framer or view finder, pick a section of the anemone to photograph and very quickly the fish will start to dart in and out of the frame. They have a habit of coming back to the same location.

Panda Clownfish
Amphiprion polmynus
60mm f2.8 / Bunaken, North Sulawesi

Male Panda Clownfish tending eggs
Amphiprion polmynus
60mm f2.8 / Bunaken, North Sulawesi

Hawkfishes
(Cirrhitidae)

Hawkfishes perch majestically on corals and rock shelves seemingly motionless and unmoved by a divers approach. Quiescent and patient, their 'hawk eyes' survey the reef for passing tiny fishes and crustaceans. When one is espied, it will swiftly swoop and pounce upon its unsuspecting prey. It is this 'Hawking' characteristic that gives this carnivorous predator its common name.

Hawkfish Identification

Though typically benthic, Hawkfishes do not bear the typical flattened, toady, or eel-like characteristics. By contrast they have a stocky body with a long, spiny dorsal fin shaped like a half moon and capped by branching "cirri" or tassels. Along with the thickened pectoral fins of most floor dwellers all species have large green or black eyes rimmed with a ring of gold.

Hawkfishes display interesting colours and designs which vary from the red cross hatch pattern of the Longnose Hawkfish (*Oxycirrhites typus*), and the red freckled face of the Blackside Hawkfish (*Paracirrhites forsteri*) to the Arc Eye Hawkfish (*Paracirrhites arcatus*) with a red, yellow and white U-shape mark around its eyes. Other colour patterns include hues of orange and red horizontal bands to the drabber colours of rock camouflage.

Hawkfishes are generally small (approx. 10cm(3")) although species of up to 22.5cm(8") have also been identified (Randall 1990).

Hawkfish Quarters

Hawkfishes peacefully reside amongst hard coral, gorgonian fans, black tree coral and rocky substratums. Without a gas bladder, you will find Hawkfishes either hawking on top of a coral branch, or hopping along the reef bottom. With their thickened lower pectoral rays they wedge themselves among corals crevices to sleep at night.

They are mainly found in tropical waters of the Indo-Pacific (3 species are found in the Atlantic waters).

Longnose Hawkfish
Oxycirrhites typus
60mm f2.8 / Bunaken, Nth. Sulawesi

Pixy Hawkfish
Cirrhitichthys oxycephalus
105mm f2.8 / Bunaken, Nth Sulawesi

Hawkfishes
(Cirrhitidae)

High Profile Sex Symbol of the Sea

Hawkfish can be found living in pairs or small groups. These fearless hunters have attributes of other such machismo reflected in their social set-up. In a male dominated society, Hawkfish live in groups comprised of one large male with several smaller females. The size of the harem varies according to the size of the territory, and may contain as many as 7 females in one coral head.

Hawkfishes spawn at dusk. The male, who has ignored his female companions all day, starts by nudging and prodding his potential partners for that evening going from one female to another. Just before dark the females move to a place on the corals sitting aloofly waiting for their 'man'. When he arrives he hops around the spawning site for a minute or so with his chosen mate before she suddenly stops and positions herself at the highest point of the coral with the male behind or beside her.

There they sit in complete "silence" side by side for about 30 seconds presumably allowing the libido level to reach its peak. At the height of the crescendo, the pair dash in unison into the water column releasing their gametes and eggs. On returning to the bottom the female then leaves the site and, if the male is lucky, he immediately moves on to the next female in the queue.

Prima Donna of the Reef

Hawkfishes are perfect models. The magic is in their eyes and they are willing sitters for portrait photography. Approach them in a non-threatening fashion and you will usually find a willing model that performs various obliging poses as you fire away.

Hawkfishes have been front cover 'models' for advertising brochures, glossy magazines and coffee table books.

Arc-Eyed Hawkfish
Paracirrhites arcatus
60mm f2.8 / Siau, Nth. Sulawesi

Falcon Hawkfish
Cirrhitichthys falco
60mm f2.8 / Great Barrier Reef, Australia

Sandperches
(Pinguipedidae)

Left to human imagination, we give names like "sea cucumber" to animals that are found slugging on the sea floor, and "starfish" to five armed animals which are not even fish! Fishes of the family of *Pinguipedidae* have a variety of names. In Australia they are called Whitings, while in Africa they are called Sand Melts, and in many countries, Sandperches or Grubfishes.

Slender Characteristics

There are more than 60 species of Sandperches in 4 genera but most of them are placed in the genus *Parapercis*. Some of them live in the deep sea but the reef dwellers are found perched on sand patches or rubble resting on their strong pelvic fins.

Small slender cigar shaped fishes they have moderately compressed elongated bodies, sharp noses, and terminal protractile mouths with canine teeth. They are frequently confused with Lizardfishes *(Synodontidae)*. The difference between the two is the longer pointed snout and flatter head of the sandperch who does not usually display his teeth.

Their bodies have a weaved pattern, typically of mottled brown, black or red on a white background and in some species males are distinguished from females by an additional dark marking on their head.

Playing, Eating and Mating on the Sand

During the day Sandperches are found either resting on the reef floor propping themselves up with their pelvic fins or enjoying a hop over the reef bed. They are territorial and on one trip we had repeated rendezvous over three days with the same three sandperches who we aptly named Nosey, Froggy and Grubby.

Though small fishes are on their menu, they would rather feed on benthic crustaceans, especially small crabs and shrimps.

Sandperches live in a 'harem' environment, Their social system is based on a male defending his own territory and the territories of his females. Mating is always within the harem, with the male selecting his companion for the evening about 40 minutes before sunset. Moving up alongside his chosen partner, he will boldly show his intentions by "bobbing" his head up and down in a mating dance. He may also hold his head over her and arouse her by fanning her with his pectoral fins. With the right chemistry, the pair will rise in unison to about 60-70cm(27-32") off the sea floor and release their sperm and eggs into the planktonic layer.

Shoot them at Eye Level

Sandperches are a fish photographer's delight. They have descriptive faces and they are easily photographed with a 60mm lens. For a great picture, shoot them at eye level.

SHARPNOSE SANDPERCH
Parapercis cylindrica
60mm f2.8 / Bitung, Nth Sulawesi

STREAKED SANDPERCH
Parapercis stricticeps
60mm f2.8 /
Nth.Coral Sea, Australia

Gobies
(Gobiidae)

Gobies are the largest family of fishes known in the tropical ocean. They are the smallest fishes in the reef and the tiniest vertebrates on earth. Even smaller than the fingernail of a little finger, it is their small size and their large numbers that make them a major player in the ecology of coral reefs.

Mistaken Identity

There are more than 1600 species of Gobies documented, with approximately 200 genera. About 1200 of these species inhabit the Indo-Pacific region. It is no wonder the different species are often mistaken for one another.

As might be expected of a huge family there are many variations in size, colour and shape. The tiniest Gobies may be less than 1cm (1/2") in length at adult size but within the family they rarely exceed 10cm(3"). Identification of such tiny subjects is difficult especially with so many closely related species.

However distinct features that identify them from other small fishes, typically the Blenny *(Blenniidae)* family, are their elongated bodies with two distinct dorsal fins and scales. They have strong pectoral fins used not only for swimming and darting about, but also in conjunction with their pelvic fin arrangements they are able to 'hop' around the sea bed.

The pelvic fin is another distinguishing feature of the Gobies. Joined at the base it forms a shallow cup which acts as a "snowshoe" supporting the body weight on very soft sediments. This is particularly useful in a surf-zone or for in-shore species, as anyone who has tried to stay put in a big swell will understand.

Home & Lifestyle

Conservative, passive creatures and plodders by nature, the gobies are one of the few marine fishes who adopt a monogamous lifestyle. Active during the day, typically you will see them in pairs (or alone) resting proudly at the entrance to their burrowed homes or scurrying about the bases of corals and rocks looking for food.

The family homes of Gobies are varied. There are species that love the open space and prefer to build their own homes, hence they are found living in burrows out on the reef bed or hovering a short distance above it (some species do occur in aggregations hovering in midwater). Other species may be found living in high rise apartments amongst hard coral plates, gorgonian fans, or hiding on the surface of sea whips or among gardens of soft corals. Some gobies are either translucent or match the camouflage colour of their habitat.

Like most of us, some Gobies (e.g. *Amblyeleotris, Cryptocentrus sp.*) do not like housework. Many Indo-Pacific species have a shrimp as a live-in maid who works through the day keeping their burrow neat and tidy and free of loose rubble and sand.

Black-Chest Shrimp Goby
Amblyeleotris guttata
105mm f2.8 / Nain, Nth Sulawesi

Elegant Fire Goby
Nemateleotris decora
105mm f2.8 / Ambon, Indonesia

Pop-eyed Gobies
Ctenogobiops promastictus
105mm f2.8 / Sangie, Nth Sulawesi

Gobies
(Gobiidae)

Whilst the maid performs its chores, the shrimp Gobies guard the burrow at the entrance. At the first sign of danger the fish will dive into the burrow and cause the fortress to collapse. Once the Goby feels safe enough to return to the entrance the shrimp begins her housework all over again.

The Arrow Goby of the U.S Pacific coast keeps a selection of labourers, from several species of worm, shrimp and sometimes the tiny pea-crab. The shrimp or pea-crab does all the housework whilst the Goby goes out hunting for food. If at the end of the day the Goby has brought home morsels that are too large to swallow whole the shrimp or crab maid is often imposed upon to perform duties of a domestic food processor. Undoubtedly shrimps or crabs are able to scavenge for the Goby's leftovers but it seems that the Gobies have a better deal in this relationship. Gobies display a wide range of diets, but most species are definite carnivores feeding mostly on tiny crabs or planktonic crustaceans. They may also eat molluscs, worms, sponges or the eggs of other fish or invertebrates, and some species act as a cleaner fish scavenging the parasites from larger free-swimming pelagics.

Pillow Talk

Heterosexual pairs that form monogamous relationships have been documented for most gobies, although some appear to spawn randomly with either many individuals or a loosely organized group. In most species the male plays the dominant role. He prepares the nest site by clearing an area on the roof of a small cave, the underside of a shell, or in their living burrow. Early in the morning he tries to entice the female to the nest by moving back and forth between her and the nest site, typically in a display of exaggerated swimming and possibly nudging her on the snout to prompt some reaction. This courtship behaviour can last up to an hour and precedes the female following the courting male back to the nest to lay her eggs.

Spawning occurs as both fish quiver frivolously side by side over the nest site, the male fertilizing each egg as she lays it. The number of demersal eggs produced depends on the species and size of female, but typically between 300-500 eggs are laid in one cluster. The eggs hatch in about 5-6 days and it is the male that performs the parental role of providing them with protection and keeping the nest clean.

A Tease for the Fish Photographer

Making pictures of Gobies teases your senses. They are small and can be pretty quick. A 105mm macro lens is an essential. When attempting to take a picture of the Gobies and shrimp, a hasty approach will spook them into diving into their burrow. Once you have spotted your subject, stop about 3m(10ft) in front of them. Frame them in your view finder and approach at a tortoise pace.

As you draw closer, expend a few frames to accustom your model to the sound of your camera and flashes. Should they withdraw into their hide-out, start all over again. Good pictures take time. To determine the best composition, it is vital to observe the gobies behaviour and movement prior to shooting.

Whip Goby
Bryaninops yongei
105mm f2.8 / Sipadan, Malaysia

Orange Dashed Gobies
Valenciennea puellaris
105mm f2.8 / Bunaken, Nth. Sulawesi

Pufferfishes
(Tetraodontidae)

On the reef the Pufferfish is the more lovable cousin of Porcupinefishes (*Diodontidae*), especially when seen resting among leathery soft coral looking like a puppy dog or a fur seal. An oddball in appearance it has the bizarre ability to instantly inflate itself to ward off predators. Puffed up and looking more like a small football waddling away from its predator the Pufferfish, or Blowfish, is often described as "cute".

Pufferfish Appearance

Most Pufferfishes are small to medium sized with scaleless skin, a beak-like mouth, a single short dorsal fin at the lower back and a similar sized anal fin below. Without pelvic fins to support its body, pufferfishes are only seen resting among sponges and soft corals. Some species don complex colour patterns but most of them are relatively drab in colour.

A family of over 100 species, they are subdivided into two distinct groups; the sharp-nosed puffers *Canthigaster* and the bulbous *Arothron*. Those in the *Canthigaster* genus are very small, rarely exceeding 12cm(5") in length, with long sharp snouts and typically colourful and striped. They are often found at the base of coral heads and crevices. The *Arothron* are larger, more rotund and solid with a seal-like appearance.

A Predator's Peril

When provoked or frightened, the pufferfish discourages would-be predators by increasing its body size by pumping water into an elastic abdominal sac from the ventral part of its stomach. To further deter advances from its predator, the pufferfish also releases, through its skin, a powerful poison called Tetraodontoxin, which is produced in its liver and ovaries.

The potent Tetraodontoxin is much stronger than cyanide. Found in the internal organs it is responsible for a number of deaths each year in eastern Asia where the fish is eaten. It is rumoured that the toxins used by the boogy-man in Haiti, to turn men into zombies, are those of the pufferfish!

In underwater encounters the pufferfish is harmless and any attempts to frighten it, so that it inflate itself, are considered un-cool.

Seal Pufferfish
Arothron nigropunctatus.
60mm f2.8 / Bunaken, Nth Sulawesi

Saddled Toby.
Canthigaster valentini
60mm f2.8 / Great Barrier Reef, Australia

Pufferfishes
(Tetraodontidae)

Habits and Diet

Pufferfishes can be found worldwide in all tropical and temperate habitats from coral and rocky reefs to seagrass beds and estuaries. The benthic reef dwellers are nocturnal and unassuming by nature, living in coral, rock, and sand, and at the outer edge of the reef during the day. Most live in pairs or in small aggregations. Sharing the same varied diet as their spiny cousin, the Porcupinefish, they use their teeth to crush the shells of their largely crustaceous diet.

Quick Sex and the Pufferfish

Many Pufferfish are group spawners, laying demersal adhesive eggs which may or may not be tended by the male. Not much is known about the spawning of the *Arothron* subfamily but research has been completed on the spawning habits of the genus *Canthigaster*.

There is thought to be a three tiered social system consisting of solitary members, pairs and harem groups within *Canthigaster* (Gladstone). Within the harem there are between 4-7 females and one dominant male who defends the territories of the group.

Spawning takes place each morning and the male selectively chooses a different female from his harem each day. The female picks the spawning site which is typically either a tuft of algae on a piece of coral or a shallow depression in the sand.

Courtship lasts up to 35 minutes in which the male follows the female with displays of exaggerated swimming, nudging her abdomen before she settles on to her nest. There she lays her stomach across the nest and in a few seconds lays hundreds of eggs whilst the male lies across or beside her and fertilizes them, departing immediately after a quick 'wham bang, thank you maam'. The female only remains at the nest site for a few minutes longer than the male, pressing and fanning the eggs before leaving and continuing her daily routine.

The incubation period is from 4 days upwards depending on water temperature, after which the larvae swim freely before settling on the bottom upon reaching adolescence.

Making Pufferfishes Pictures

Pufferfishes are easily photographed when they are found resting almost motionless among corals and sponges during the day and night. You can approach pretty close without them being frightened away. Catching them on the move is a little trickier, but it is possible to preempt their moves after a short period of observation.

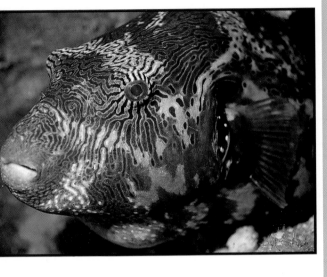

Map Pufferfish
Arothron mappa.
60mm f2.8 / Bunaken, Nth Sulawesi

Solander Toby.
Canthigaster solandri
60mm f2.8 / Great Barrier Reef, Australia

PORCUPINEFISHES
(Diodontidae)

Looking at the Porcupinefish it is easy to see where this short, rotund, rather comical character derives its name. Commonly known as the Balloonfish, Burrfish or Spiny Puffer it is easily identifiable by the spines covering its head and body and one of the only fish families that can be seen slowly waddling, rather than swimming through the water.

A Sharp Character!

A Porcupinefish has the unique ability to inflate itself into a ball shape by filling its abdomen with water when danger threatens. When inflating itself, sharp spines point outwards as an additional deterrent against would-be predators. With this effective defense system they do not need to be good or fast swimmers and appear to waddle along in a rather funny fashion, propelling themselves with their soft dorsal and anal fins. Despite their effective armour of spines they are passive. However when pushed or tormented be warned, they are capable of inflicting a severe bite. Found in both tropical and temperate seas there are about 19 species to this family of small to medium size fish. Larger oceanic fishes like marlins, sharks and tunas feed on juvenile porcupinefishes often at their own peril. We once found a dead 8 foot long marlin with an inflated porcupinefish stuck in its throat.

The Lone Ranger of the Reef

Found at the reef bottom up to depths of 30m(100ft) or more, these timid fishes usually lead a solitary life. Many are nocturnal, retiring into caves, hiding beneath ledges, or hovering quietly in some sheltered area during the day. If you do see Porcupinefish in the morning light, their droopy eyes makes them look like they have been awake all night.

Opportunistic predators they feed on a varied diet of organisms from the ocean floor. Using their shearing teeth and powerful jaws they crush the shells of their staple diet of sea urchins, molluscs, crabs, hermit crabs and snails to feed on the soft tissues inside.

Breeding Pains

Porcupinefishes spawn in pairs or in a group of several males to one female. The male starts the courtship by following the female, occasionally nudging her abdomen. After a while, if she is receptive to his advances, she then ascends further off the bottom with the male trailing behind. When sufficiently aroused, the mating process becomes a little rougher as the male pushes the female to the surface by pressing his snout against her abdomen, where she sheds her eggs as he releases his sperm.Their off-spring spend some time floating as planktonic larvae before settling to the bottom to undertake the responsibilities of adulthood.

Porcupinefishes are Perfect Models

They are slow swimmers and they have beautiful eyes! This does not mean that you should catch one to take a picture of an inflated balloon. It is a pretty un-cool thing to do as well as being environmentally unfriendly, and the fish won't be too keen on the idea either! The best time to take a photograph of porcupinefishes is at night or in the early morning where they tend to be a little dreamy. Simply observe their swimming path and position youself to capture the perfect shot.

Freckled Porcupine-Fish
Diodon holocanthus
60mm f2.8 / Bunaken, Nth Sulawesi

Rounded Porcupine-Fish
Cyclichthys orbicularis
60mm f2.8 / Komodo, Indonesia

The Ocean,
an Awesome
place for a
Lifetime
of
Observation
(ma)

Hole and Crevice Residents

Free Roving Fishes that are usually found in holes and crevices of the coral reef

Eels
(Muraenidae)

There are 110 species of Moray Eels and they are among the elite and infamous inhabitants of all coral reefs in the world. Their reputation as ferocious killers that stalk and attack divers, has been sensationalised on the silver screen. Nothing could be further from the truth. Moray eels are shy and retiring animals who lead a secret life beneath the chambers of the sea.

An 'Eely' Appearance

Moray eels are distinctive and easily identifiable by their disposition, colour, pattern and their body size. Looking more like a snake with its elongated muscularly compressed body, the eel is actually a fish with one long ribbon dorsal fin which often melts into the anal fins and tail, and no pectoral fins.

Among fishes however they are 'odd balls'. The vertical slit gills of other fish are replaced with a couple of holes on each side of their body situated several inches behind their small head. With two protruding tubular nostrils, moray eels possess an advanced sense of smell. They are also equipped with long fang-like canine teeth and their scaleless body is covered with mucus. Just like their earthier counterpart, they swim in a zigzag motion resembling a snake grazing in the grass.

Colour and size variation ranges from the drab brown Giant Moray (*Gymnothorax javanicus*) which can reach 220cm(8.5ft) in length and weigh about 29kg(63 lbs), to the beautiful extremely elongated fluorescent blue Ribbon Eels (*Rhinomuraena quaesita*) which only reach a maximum length of 65cm(30").

An 'Eels-Abused' Reputation

Moray eels are found in holes and small crevices among coral and rubble with their head poking out of their lair. They seem to be singing a silent song with their mouth opening and closing; actually they are inhaling water, passing the water through their gills and gill holes.

It is this open mouth breathing technique, and sharp canine teeth fully visible to the observer, that earns them a ferocious reputation.

Morays are fairly docile and non-aggressive but they will bite when harassed and, quite understandably, they are known to fiercely defend their 'castles' and their lives.

Putting your hand into their domain, among holes and caves, is an invasion of their privacy and most likely you will be attacked. Once bitten your natural reaction of pulling your finger or hand out from their mouth of fanged teeth will result in severe lacerations requiring surgical stitches. In this situation it is better to stay still, wait for their mouth to open again of its own accord (which it has to do to breathe) and you will probably suffer only a few puncture wounds instead.

Feeding moral eels is an invitation for trouble. Reputed to have bad eyesight they may well mistake your ears, nose and hair for morsels of food.

GIANT MORAY
Gymnothorax javanicus
60 f2.8 / GREAT BARRIER REEF, AUSTRALIA

Blue Ribbon Eel
Rhinomuraena quaesita
60mm f2.8 / BUNAKEN, Nth SULAWESI

Eels
(Muraenidae)

Eel Habits

Eels live a solitary life only leaving their lair to roam the reef at night in search of food. Carnivorous by nature, they feed on octopus, shrimps, mussels, lobsters, and small fish. Some moray eels have developed pharyngeal jaws that allow them to crush hard shells of mussels, clams and crustaceans.

When fish is on the menu, they use their fanged teeth to firmly grip their food. Without chewing the fish, they reposition the fish to point towards their throat head first. This prevents the fish's dorsal fins from sticking in their throat and choking them. In one "whoosh" the entire fish is swallowed whole and the moray will spend the rest of the evening digesting its meal. We once witnessed a giant moray swallowing a porcupinefish in one gulp! - what a stomach ache he must have had that evening!

Morays are also known to scavenge for dead fish and often attempt to enter fish traps for a free feed on fish bait.

Eel Affairs

The reproductive behaviour of eels is a well kept secret. Complete accounts and observations of mating pairs are too few to be conclusive. Courtship behaviour is believed to vary between genera and includes swimming singularly or in groups near the surface.

On one occasion we sighted a pair of white spotted morays (*Gymnothorax meleagris*) entwined on the bottom of a reef flat in North Sulawesi. In conjunction with the accounts published by Brocks and Yamamoto (1972) a possible scenario would suggest that a pair of eels leave their holes and slowly approach one another on the reef bottom.

There they possibly stop at eels length, then together raise their bodies, with their mouths open and dorsals erect. After a brief puff of silent songs they embrace and finally fall back to lie on the bottom entwined, ultimately pressing their abdomens together and releasing a cloud of gametes at the height of their communion.

Taking Eel Photographs

Morays will often retreat into their holes when approached. Stop at a short distance and let them become accustomed to your presence and get acquainted by firing off a few frames.

With a little gentle encouragement they are great for close up photographs. As a nocturnal fish, they are livelier at night and a full body shot is often possible then.

Darkspotted Moray
Gymnothorax moray
60mm f2.8 / Ambon, Indonesia

Starry Moray
Echidna nebulosa
60mm f2.8 /Bunaken, Nth Sulawesi

Squirrelfishes
(Holocentridae)

If you see a red fish beneath a coral ledge or cave with ridiculously big round bulbous eyes, it is probably a Squirrelfish or a Soldierfish. It is assumed that from these large eyes, Squirrelfishes derived their common name. Or it may be from their timid nature and ability to dart away and hide at the first sign of danger, resembling the characteristics of their terra firma counterpart.

Squirrelfishes Details

Often a prolific sight at night, Squirrelfishes and Soldierfishes are among the most abundant of the nocturnally active reef fishes. From a family of 70 species in 8 genera, their red colour, or shades thereof, and large eyes make them easily recognizable. The species Big-eye or Scarlet Soldierfish *(Myripristis pralinia)* is commonly observed on reefs and they have the biggest eyes in the family.

Other clues of identification include their large rough scales, pronounced forked tail, and a relatively large mouth. They are medium-sized fish generally between 15-35cm(6-15").

The species of the *Sargocentron* genera are usually striped, often territorial, and their defence system includes a large spine at the corner of the preopercle which is lacking in soldierfishes. Though not as severe as that of a Scorpionfish *(Scorpaenidae),* the squirrelfish's spine is venomous and can inflict painful wounds if provoked. We once witnessed a diver suffer temporary paralysis for 4 hours after suffering a wound of this nature. The Samurai Squirrelfish *(Sargocentron microstoma)* is a good example of this genus. (see picture)

Homefront

Most species are found in shallow waters on rocky bottoms or on coral reefs in tropical waters in depths of 30m(100ft) although some live in depths of up to 200m(656ft). They can be found in most tropical waters around the world, especially near the equator, though some species prefer the cooler subtropical waters.

Their large eyes suggest most species are nocturnal. During the day they will elude the underwater observer by hiding in caves or crevices or under ledges. They emerge at night and swim either in pairs or small to large groups foraging for food along the reef. An unusual sight, you may occasionally see them swimming upside-down beneath coral plates and caverns.

Whitetip Soldierfish
Myripristis vittata
60mm f2.8 / Bunaken, Nth Sulawesi

Sammara Squirrelfish
Neoniphon sammara
60mm f2.8 / Great Barrier Reef, Australia

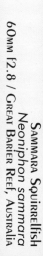

Squirrelfishes
(Holocentridae)

What's for dinner tonight?
Meal time is after dark. Squirrelfishes and soldierfishes sustain life by feeding on small fishes and invertebrates. Exceptions to the rule include the genus of *Myripristis* which feeds on larger elements of plankton whilst the genus of *Sargocentron* mainly feeds on benthic crabs and shrimps.

Secrets Sex
Little is known about the rituals of courtship and the sexual activity of Squirrelfish. Except for a few observations of possible courtship behaviour, nothing is conclusive. Since they are usually found in small groups, it may not be too far out to suggest that they participate in group spawning at dusk or in the early evening.

Squirrelfishes Pictures
Squirrelfish are best photographed at night while they are out foraging through the reef. Approach cautiously to avoid spooking them into crevices.. Use a slow speed film, such as Fuji Velvia to bring out their colours.

Squirrelfish Beneath Coral Plate
Sargocentron sp.
60mm f2.8 / Cebu, Philippines

Samurrai Squirrelfish
Sargocentron mircostoma
60mm f2.8 / Bunaken, Nih. Sulawesi

Cardinalfishes
(Apogonidae)

After sundown Cardinalfishes come out to play. Although only small in size they certainly make up for it in number and variety. Predominantly silvery and translucent-like, they resemble Christmas lights flickering on the coral reefs at night. Their common name, derived from their red coloration, is very misleading as a huge number of the species are yellow, brown, black, blue tint, and silver to goldish orange.

Cardinalfish Features

Important characteristics of cardinalfishes are their large scales and large mouths, designed for brooding offspring. Their bodies are laterally compressed with two separate dorsal fins and a long tail base. Particular species are easily identifiable by distinctive markings of stripes, spots, and colouration. Most of them are lightly coloured and a few species have bacterial luminescent organs which make them glow in the dark.

Cardinalfishes are among the smallest fish in the ocean, but there are a few 'giants' among them growing to 22cm(10"). There are about 250 species in 23 genera worldwide. The majority of them are found in the Indo-Pacific basin. Most species belong to the genus *Apogon* and can generally be found during the day beneath corals, in sandy reef lagoons, in crevices of deep slopes, among coral trees, and in ship wrecks. Some species are known to inhabit ledges in deeper water.

A few smaller species are known to have developed close living arrangements with other toxic animals like the Urchin Cardinalfish (*Sphaeramia versicolor*) that lives among sea urchins (Eibl-Eibesfeldt), and the Crown-of-Thorns Cardinalfish (*Siphamia fuscolineata*) who lives with the Crown of Thorns sea star (Allen 1972).

The Lifestyle of Cardinalfishes

Cardinalfishes rest together in the day, but when evening comes they will either wander the reef alone or split off into small groups or pairs. Some species (*Rhabdamia sp.*) congregate in thousands and generally hang out within a wreck or reef corridors.

Cardinalfishes are the nocturnal equivalent of the diurnal Damselfishes (*Pomacentridae*). If you see a fish wandering about in the open at night, it will probably be a cardinalfish. Some species prefer to dine alongside basketstars and gorgonian fans.

Their dietary habits vary from species to species and most of them love to feast on zooplankton and small benthic animals such as small shrimps and crabs.

Ringtail Cardinalfish
Apogon aureus.
105mm f2.8 / Dayang, Malaysia

Samoan Cardinalfish
Apogon fucus
105mm f2.8 / Bunaken, Nih Sulawesi

CARDINALFISHES
(Apogonidae)

Courting Females

In the society of *Apogon* Cardinalfishes it is the female who initiates the lengthy courtship which may even take all night. Once a female has selected her partner she will begin the courtship by swimming closely by his side. The pair will soon move in a circular pattern with her on the outside and the male on the inside.

Should they be interrupted they will both split off, but quickly return to their circling behaviour. This may continue throughout the night and gradually, with increasing passion, the male will wrap his anal fins around his companion's abdomen (Garnaud 1960).

The height of the union is signalled by the pair quivering side by side as masses of egg balls are released by the female and simultaneously fertilized by the male. Cardinalfish eggs are gelatinous and bind together in a tight ball.

Mouthoven! A Mother's best friend

Just when you think that they have a better deal, it is the responsibility of the male to tend to his offspring by engulfing them in his mouth. A brooding father can easily be distinguished by his swollen throat region and the eggs can be seen when he periodically juggles them for aeration.

During the incubation period, from 8-17 days, the male starves while the female stands by to defend her brooding companion. After hatching the larvae remain in the planktonic layer for several weeks before settling on the reef.

The Cardinalfish's Portrait

Approaching this little razzle dazzle of the reef is not a problem at night. They will generally remain still and pose while you settle down to compose your picture. Watch strobe positioning as their colouration tends to be reflective. Flaring occurs when the fish are moving especially during group pictures.

Iridescent Cardinalfish (this one mouth-brooding his eggs)
Apogon kallopterus
105mm f2.8 / Bunaken Nth. Sulawesi

Goldbelly Cardinalfish
Apogon apogonides (courtship sequence)
105mm f2.8 / Bali, Indonesia

JAWFISHES
(Opistognathidae)

An incognito among coral reef fishes and the 'mole' of the underworld, Jawfishes live in underground burrows on open reef patches. Its secretive lifestyle has evaded discovery of but a few known species. There are probably quite a few of them scurrying around beneath the world's oceans. Now that the secret is out, new species are being identified regularly.

Big Mouth!

Jawfishes have big mouths and an enlarged toady heads. Besides being used for eating, their big mouth is an essential tool for home building and indeed for ensuring the very continuity of their species, by providing an in-built incubator.

They have big round bulging eyes, usually black, and their body colouration is mostly dullish white, grey, brown or yellow. Generally it is a small fish of less than 10cm(4") but large jawfishes reaching lengths of 50cm(23") have been recorded.

A Self Taught Home Builder

Jawfishes are found living alone in their self built burrows on the reef bed. Although they are found in individual burrows, a Jawfish community can be found with burrows situated in close proximity.

In the world of fish, Jawfishes' home engineering and maintenance skills are rather complex. After selecting a site they clear the area by scooping and spitting out unwanted materials with their jaws. Even shifting larger rocks is performed using these powerful jaws. Excavating the burrow then begins, again using their mouths. Once the burrow is complete the final stage involves building a wall of neatly stacked pebbles, coral pieces or shells around their fortress. A home is built in about 8 hours and if a major catastrophe occurs causing their home to collapse, home building or restructuring begins immediately.

If you see a Jawfish away from its burrow, they are often leaving home to gather raw materials to reinforce their fortress, or dumping unwanted fragments into their neighbour's backyard.

When not performing their domestic chores, time is spent at the entrance of the burrow feeding on passing planktonic or benthic invertebrates. After the effort they put into building their own home, it is not surprising that they are extremely territorial and will vigorously defend the vicinity of their burrow.

Jawfishes are rare in the Australian Great Barrier Reef. The Gold Rim Jawfish (*Opistognathus sp.*) featured on the facing page is a new species still awaiting description by scientists. It is frequently sighted from Ambon to Bali, Bunaken, and Toli-Toli in Indonesia. We spent a few days watching this little fish burrow building and coexisting with neighbouring mates.

Gold-Specs Jawfish ~ busy with burrow cleaning and reinforcing chores. *Opistognathus* sp. (new species to science, widespread over Indonesia) 105mm f2.8 / Bunaken, Nth. Sulawesi

Mouthing Offsprings

Leading a secret lifestyle, Jawfishes courtship behaviour has only been vaguely recorded, however the genera *Aurifrons* has been studied in detail. They are sometimes assumed to mate heterogeneously at random but could also be monogamous. The Atlantic Yellow Jawfish (*Opistognathus aurifrons*) has been observed in a permanent relationship, mating regularly and helping clean his partner's burrow, and vice versa (Colin 1972).

From what is known it appears that sexual advances are made by the male hovering over the female burrow displaying courtship colours. The courting sequence varies with species but generally he hovers for 3-5 seconds before returning to his burrow. For some species this song and dance may need to be repeated every 4-5 minutes and may continue for an hour.

When sufficiently aroused and ready, the female follows the male back to his burrow where spawning takes place inside. This is the only time that the female and male share the same burrow in otherwise separate lives.

It is the male who performs the parental duties by brooding the eggs in his big mouth. With the eggs protruding from his jaws he ensures adequate ventilation by occasionally agitating them back and forth in his mouth. It is assumed that he settles the eggs down in his burrow when he takes a break for feeding time. Hatching occurs between 7 to 9 days later when the male releases the eggs in the water. The larvae settle back down to the reef floor in about 15 days where they are immediately recognizable as jawfish. Even at about 10mm to 15mm(1/3-5/8") in size they begin burrowing their own homes.

Go Away, No One is Home!

There are many photographers who have never seen a jawfish. They might find a burrow, but the Jawfish is never home. The truth is that some Jawfish have a blackish face and at a distance this will look like an empty hole or, as they are very shy, they retreat quickly when approached.

To successfully photograph Jawfishes, first look for round holes with a fortress of coral pieces on a sandy reef patch. Once spotted, stay at a distance of at least 3m(10ft) and wait patiently. If you are lucky you will see a little fellow emerging from his hole performing some house cleaning chores. An 105mm macro lens is a must!

Gold-Specs Jawfish ~ this little fellow took over 6 hours to refurbish his home. *Opistognathus sp.* (new species to science, widespread over Indonesia) 105mm f2.8 / Toli Toli, Nth. Sulawesi

BLENNIES
(Blennidae)

Blennies are one of the tiniest fish on the reef and are frequently mistaken for Gobies. With a large fleshy cheek, often bulbous eyes and toady or froggy appearance they are affectionately described as cute. With over 270 species to their name they are bottom dwellers that inhabit the foreshore, reef flat and slopes of tropical and temperate waters.

An Odd Character

Blennies are blunt headed with their mouths situated low on their heads and many have bizarre fringed or branched tentacles (cirri) protruding from their forehead. All Blennies are scaleless with one long continuous dorsal fin and their pelvic fins are clearly anterior to the pectoral fin.

Apart from swimming and darting around, their strong pectoral fin arrangements are used for balancing on the reef. Some species that live on the inter-tidal zone are capable of leaping from rock pool to rock pool hence their given name of Rock or Mudskipper (eg.*Entomacrodus sp.*).

A Bohemian Lifestyle

Unlike Gobies who build their own burrows and enjoy monogamous relationships, Blennies prefer to adopt a bohemian singular lifestyle with little time for domesticity. Found in depths of up to 25m(80ft) they live in coral crevices and holes and they will only build a nest if there are females to entice. Their hideouts are usually small and they have the habit of entering backwards, tail first. In the day, Blennies can be located either watching the world go by from inside their quarters or perching on the indoor step.

Con-artists of the Reef

Though most of the tropical species are herbivorous, some feed on coral polyps and small crustaceans as well as zooplankton and eggs of other fishes.

A few of their members, however, give the Blenny family a bad reputation. The Sabretooth Blennies (*Plagiotremus and Aspidontus sp.*) are prime examples. Being of similar colouration to the Cleaner Wrasse (*Labroides dimidiatus*), they are able to mimic the harmless Cleaning Wrasse to get closer to their prey. Having fooled its unsuspecting prey it then uses two enormous canine teeth in its lower jaw to attack the fish, feeding on its scales, mucus and dermal tissues.

Other Blennies have jumped onto the mimicking habits of their sabretooth cousins. The Lyre-tail or Cleopatra Eyes Blenny (*Meiacanthus sp.*) is the boldest of the family and is equipped with venomous fangs for defence purposes. It is no wonder that they feel bold enough to hover way off the bottom as predators have learnt to avoid them. Other 'copycat' species, including *Plagiotremus, Petroscirtes, and Ecsenius sp.*, impersonate this venomous fanged species in order to deceive predators.

Orange Bath Comb-tooth Blenny
Ecsenius bathi
105mm f2.8 / Ambon, Indonesia

Orange-spotted Leopard Blenny
Exallias brevis.
60mm f2.8 / Bunaken, Nth Sulawesi

BLENNIES
(Blennidae)

Role Reversal

Contrary to "traditional" behaviour, in Blenny society it is the female that initiates courtship but the male that provides the maternal duties of tending and defending eggs. Spawning activity varies with species but always occurs during the day near the male domain.

The female, in her courtship colours, begins the process by passing in front of the male lair. In some species the male might swim towards the female in an up and down sinussoidal motion while in other species the male will just pose at the entrance of his hole and perform the Blenny courtship rite of head 'bobbing' (shaking his head vigorously up and down).

Once the male feels that he has successfully aroused his partner he will try to lead her to his nest, or sit in front and signal her towards it whilst continuing to '**bob**' his head. Subject to a satisfactory inspection of his den, she then parks herself (bottom first) into it and lays her eggs. If the site is large enough the male will sit side by side undulating with her in unison; as she lays her eggs he fertilizes them. Otherwise he sits outside to drive away any intruder still 'bobbing' and pops back in to fertilize the eggs at regular intervals.

The process lasts from a few minutes to half a day, in some species, producing between 100-160 eggs (Fishelson 1975). The female Orange Spotted Blenny (*Exallias brevis)* spawns regularly every three to four days, producing an average of 200,000 - 300,000 eggs per year.
The demersal eggs are generally large and hatch in about nine days with the male aerating them vigorously during hatching time.

Now You See Me, Now You Don't

I must have loved this Blenny, having once spent up to four hours trying to take a picture of a pregnant Banded Blenny. This little super intelligent trickster seems to have the aptitude to pre-empt every move, confounding me with an artful routine of disappearing acts.

Even with a pre-focusing technique, they will sit still long enough for composition, but will retreat into their hole just as you are about to depress the shutter. To outwit blennies, I carry an extra camera with lots of film. Patience is a pre-requisite and do not be surprised if you resort to praying and talking to the fish.

White Spotted Blenny
Ecsenius triliatus
105mm f2.8 / Ambon, Indonesia

Cleopatra-Eyes Blenny
Meiacanthus atrodorsalis
60mm/ f2.8 GBR, Australia

Bluestriped Fang Blenny
Plagiotremus rhinorhynchos.
105mm f2.8 / Nain, Nth Sulawesi

We would specially like to thanks **Dr. Gerald Allen** for scientific advise, editing and photographic identification. Gerry, it is a thrill just to dive in the same ocean with you. Thanks too, to **Maria Kavallaris & Sophia Symeou** for editing and opinions. It is much appreciated and valued. Our love and heartfelt thanks to **Sidney Seok** for your involvement; the late nights, the early morning calls and for being there even though you are over 8000 kms away. Your simple manner as a human being and love for your family and friends has impressed us immensely.

ACKNOWLEDGEMENTS

We would also like to thank **Dr. Hanny and Ineke Batuna** for diving and the logistical support that made this book possible. You have inspired this production. A sincere thank you to **Sandra Hejtmanek** for coming in at the final hours and helping us wrap up this book, you are a gem! Big warm hugs to **Mae Senduk**, thank you for your tireless assistance. All the crew at **Colour Development,** thank you for bringing out the best possible colours! We are also fortunate to have the assistance of **Lena Sum and Josephine Woodward**. Our warmest gratitude and special thanks. **To all that have helped** and who we have inadvertenly omitted to mention, We thank you. **Most of all our thanks to God, for the 'Electric energy and keeping the Dream alive!**

Recommended Reading:
Indo-Pacific Coral Reef Field Guide- Dr. Gerald R.Allen & Roger Steen
Tropical Reef Fishes-ISBN 981-00-5687-7
Tropical Reef Fishes Indonesian and Adjacent Waters, R. Kuiter
P.T. Gramedia ISBN 979-511-058-6
Fishes of GRB and Coral Sea, J.Randall, G. Allen, R.Steen,
Crawford House ISBN 1-86333-012-7
Beneath Bunaken, a Pictorial Anthology, Michael AW,
OCEAN Geographic ISBN 0-646-15511-3
Reproduction in Reef Fishes Dr. R.E. Thresher,
TFH Publications ISBN 0-87666-808-2

"Beneath Bunaken"
by MichaelAW

is a celebration of one of nature's most pristine underwater wildernesses. In the form of an almanac, it presents 182 award winning marine images covering twenty-four hours in the life of the Bunaken marine park, from sunrise to the late night hours. No expense is spared in its production. Cased bound with expensive six color printing, it comes with its own slip case. It is now used by many Indonesian Government provinces and consulates as an official Gift of state.

Proceeds of this book will help to purchase mooring blocks for the marine park to prevent damage to the reef.

"Your book is fantastic! It should be a big hit!" Marjorie Bank, USA.

"It is a great joy to have viewed this beautiful book, " Robert Dielman, USA

"A superb pictorial survey of the coral reef of Bunaken, one of the finest marine parks in the world." The Telegraph Mirror, Sydney

"Every single one of the beautifully-reproduced colour photographs is a visual treat as rich on the eye as beluga caviare is on the palate and not nearly so hard to acquire a taste for." Garuda Infight Magazine, Indonesia

" 'Beneath Bunaken' is one of the world's prettiest books of underwater photographs." Becca Saunders, Australia

Strictly limited edition. For an author autographed copy contact your nearest book shop or the publisher of this publication.

about the Authors

Ambon Is. Indonesia

Michael AW is a photo-journalist, based in Sydney, he specialize in natural history, environment and travel features. His articles and photographs have been featured in publications spanning from Australia and East Asia to the United States, and include 'GEO', 'Ocean Realm' (USA), 'Discover Diving' (USA), 'Sport Diving', 'Scuba Diving', and 'Sojourns'.

Michael and Laura often work as a writing team and they also manage **Ocean Discoverers,** a group dedicated to preserving and protecting the quality of the marine environment. Ocean Discoverers is a self-funded organization involved in exploration of and education about coral reef and marine life. They share their discoveries in their published works and lectures to promote better awareness with the hope to increase everyone's affinity with the animals of the sea.

Michael Aw is also the author of the award winning pictorial anthology 'Beneath Bunaken' - **"A jump for the joy of living, A spring of celebration in being, Taking the air at the top of the world, A Quantum leap for Human beings who begin to know the Nature of the Sea"**

(Extracts from BB)